HELP AT HAND

Jane Brotchie has worked as a trainer and tutor with people with special needs. She was a founder member of Carousel, a Brighton-based project which works alongside people with learning difficulties using creative arts. In 1986 she began working with people caring at home when she joined the East Sussex Carers' Demonstration District, a three-year programme funded by the Department of Health to set up support and services for carers. During this time she helped set up the Hove Carer's Centre and contributed articles to the national and specialist press.

She maintains an interest in the voluntary sector as a member of the executive committee of the local council for voluntary service. She currently works as a freelance writer and journalist, specialising in women's concerns, social policy and health issues.

HELP AT HAND

The Home Carers' Survival Guide

Jane Brotchie

Bedford Square Press

Published by
BEDFORD SQUARE PRESS of the
National Council for Voluntary Organisations
26 Bedford Square, London WC1B 3HU

First published 1990

Typeset by BookEns, Saffron Walden, Essex
Printed and bound in Great Britain by
Southampton Book Company, Southampton

British Library Cataloguing in Publication Data
Brotchie, Jane
  Help at hand.
  1. Great Britain. Dependent persons. Home care
  I. Title II. Series
  649.8

ISBN 0-7199-1281-2

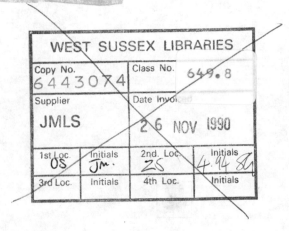

Contents

Acknowledgements

My thanks to all those who helped this book on its way. My first and heartfelt thanks goes to all the carers who have talked with me and written to me about their experiences. I have felt privileged to hear your stories of courage, compassion and honesty, painful though it has been at times. Thanks to Mandy Edwards, Helen Bashford and all the workers, carers and volunteers at the Hove Carers Centre, especially to Helen Armstrong, Lola Frost and Edie Badiali; to the Carers National Association for their ready help; to the editors of *The Carer* and *BACUP News*, for permission to quote from their newsletters; to the Health Education Authority for permission to reprint the extract on pages 42–3 from *Working with Carers* (1989) by Rosie Bell and Sue Gibbons; to Macmillan Education for permission to reprint the extract on pages 88–9 from *Sweet Adeline: A Journey Through Care* (1988) by Patricia Slack and Frank Mulville; to Thames Television for permission to adapt material on pages 106–8 from *The Treatment: A Guide to Choosing an Old People's Home*; and to the National Council for the Aged, Dublin for permission to adapt material from *Carers: You Matter Too!* by Prof. Joyce O'Connor and Dr Helen Ruddle; to Mary Colato at the East Sussex Care for the Carers Council and to Carol Youngs at Contact a Family for their comments on the manuscript; to Jean Wooller and the Polegate carers; to Ian Bynoe at MIND and Gary Vaux at Brent Social Services for their specialist help; to Jonathan Croall and Jacqueline Sallon for their guidance as editors; to my friend Christopher Robbins for giving me the confidence to write it in the first place; and to Deborah Clow and Philippa Cannan for their constant wisdom and support.

1 Introduction

Why a survival guide?

You may not think of yourself as 'a carer'. It may seem only natural to take on the care of a parent, a child or a partner when they fall ill or are disabled. Perhaps you feel it deserves no special recognition. After all, you know how much the person you look after has had to suffer.

Carers are people like you or me: ordinary people who are thrust into extraordinary circumstances by looking after a relative, friend or partner in the home.

But the chances are that, if you have been doing this for any length of time, you will have encountered a number of obstacles. Either the professional help has not been there when you have needed it – or you may feel torn between the demands of caring, work, family and keeping your own life going.

This is one reason why people who care at home have started to see themselves as a group with similar interests, even when the people they care for have different conditions or impairments. With the help of local and national voluntary organisations, such as the Carers National Organisation, Contact a Family, the Alzheimer's Disease Society and the National Schizophrenia Fellowship, carers are joining forces to press for more recognition and support.

People who are carers often feel that the difficulties they experience are part and parcel of taking on the care of a relative, and to complain is somehow to admit to failure as a 'caring person'. But nobody should have to carry out strenuous nursing and daily personal tasks for another person every day of the year without a break or any assistance. Many carers do just that.

The failure of successive governments to provide adequate and appropriate support for people with disabilities and their carers has meant that many thousands of people are left to struggle alone, finding help more by chance than design.

Carers need public and professional support and this is often sadly lacking. The efforts of campaigning organisations are beginning to bear fruit and there is a much greater awareness of the need for practical help for carers. As I write, an important piece of legislation for carers is under discussion (the White Paper *Caring for People: Community Care in the Next Decade and Beyond*). While we wait for this awareness to be translated into practical help, many people are still faced with impossible choices in their lives.

Not everybody is able to take on caring responsibilities, even if they wish to. It should be a choice, freely made, but very rarely is. For a working woman with young children the choices may be stark if an elderly parent falls ill and she is expected to cope. The family may need her income to get by. Does she give up work or arrange alternative care? What if that care is not available or not up to the standard she can accept? Whose needs come first: her mother's, her family's, her own?

'Care' cannot be sustained in a vacuum – it is not only a private 'family' concern, an extension of domestic duty. It is a public responsibility. Many carers give their love and labour willingly. But because of their personal feelings of love and duty, they have to suffer the inadequacies of a society that is not organised to care for its more vulnerable members.

How to use this book

This book is written with the understanding that services are far from perfect and that if you are a carer, you will probably have to struggle to get what you need. But it is not all bleak: there are some very good services available to carers in some parts of the country and there are many social workers, community nurses and doctors who are aware of your need for support. The problem is finding them!

The message from other carers is that help is rarely freely offered – you need to ask. But before you can ask for help, you need to know what the right questions are and who to address them to. This book will give you some guidance.

The emphasis all the way through is on you, the carer. By this, I do not mean to suggest that the person who is ill or disabled is in any way less important. In many cases, what helps the person you look after will also help you, but the habit of caring for someone else means it is easy to neglect your own needs.

You will find that you are not alone in your dilemmas. Reading a book may be a second best to getting out and meeting people who can give you help and emotional back up. But if leaving the house is difficult, or you find some things too hard to talk to others about, you will find tips and information to help both you and the person you look after.

Carers' individual experiences illustrate many of the points raised in the book. You will find a lot of emphasis is given to how you *feel* about caring. This is because caring takes place in the context of personal relationships and feelings can often be complex and sometimes distressing. I believe that it helps to understand this and to know that others may have similar reactions. But there are no hard and fast rules: no right and wrong ways to feel or act. Carers have much in common, but everyone's story is different.

If you don't have much time or energy for reading, you don't need to read from cover to cover. Not all of the book will be relevant to you: just dip in, take what is useful and ignore what is not.

You are not alone: some facts about carers

According to 1988 statistics, the Family Policy Studies Centre estimated that the care provided by people caring for people at home saves the state between 15 and 24 billion pounds per year.

Two further reports* add to what we know about carers and people with disabilities:

- One adult in seven in Britain is a carer. Overall this adds up to over six million, with 1.7 million caring for someone in the same household.
- Women are more likely to be carers than men: 3.5 million compared with 2.5 million.
- Almost a quarter of carers (24 per cent) are spending at least 20 hours a week caring, with around 60 per cent of these spending at least 50 hours.
- Of those spending at least 20 hours a week caring, nearly one third have dependent children and nearly one half of those of working age are in paid employment.

*OPCS General Household Survey 1985, *Informal Carers*, HMSO, 1988 and OPCS *The Prevalence of Disability among Adults*, HMSO, 1988.

- Many carers are in ill-health themselves: about one half of those aged 45 or over reporting a long-standing illness.
- There are six million adults (14 per cent of the adult population) with disabilities in Britain. More than 93 per cent are living in private households (i.e. in the community) rather than in communal or institutional care.
- 70 per cent of all disabled people are over 60 and the very elderly predominate among the most severely disabled.

Part I
Understanding Caring

2 The ups and downs of caring

'I don't ever switch off completely. You're on duty 24 hours a day.'

What does it mean to be a 'carer'?

Looking after someone who is ill or disabled at home can affect your health, family and social life, and your finances. It may be something you want to do, but you need and deserve support *yourself* to preserve your own health and well-being.

There is no 'typical' carer: we are all likely to become carers at some time in our lives.

Perhaps you are looking after an elderly relative after being discharged from hospital following a serious illness. Perhaps you are a parent looking after a child with special needs. Or you may be looking after your partner who has a chronic illness. It may be a lifetime's commitment or a matter of a few weeks. Or, with some conditions, you may not know how long you will be caring.

Not all caring takes place under the same roof: you could be regularly travelling 50 miles to see to the needs of a friend recovering from a car accident. If that person cannot manage without your help, you are a carer.

Coming to terms with illness, sudden disability and physical suffering is hard for everyone. If the entire responsibility for physical care seems to fall to you there will be times when the emotional and physical demands appear overwhelming. There are few easy answers when you are trying to maintain a good quality of life for somebody who is dependent on your help for daily living.

The current use of the word 'caring' has come to mean home nursing and all the activities associated with looking after a person in the home. But of course, 'caring' starts with a set of feelings that describe love and concern for the well-being of another person.

Caring about a relative's welfare does not automatically mean you should take on all aspects of their day-to-day physical needs. You may not be very good at it for one thing – but the pressure of our own and other people's expectations to do so are often very hard to resist. Often there appears to be no choice.

Women may feel a particular sense of duty to step in and be the 'carer' because caring, in its practical sense, is seen as a natural extension of women's domestic role as mother, nurturer and care-giver. But not all women are cut out for this kind of work and many already have other demands (of family or work) which make it very difficult to assume the responsibility for another person.

This is not to say that everyone who is caring for a person at home is coerced into doing so. Many women want to provide care and do so willingly, but because of society's assumptions about women's 'caring nature', they may be left to cope alone with work that would occupy several staff on shifts in a hospital.

Men who become carers are more likely to be looking after a partner or wife than a distant relative. For those men who have had active working lives, the role of carer demands difficult adjustments because the work that carers do tends not be recognised or accorded much status.

What are the rewards?

These are the things that sustain carers through the difficult times:

I cared for my mother until her death at 100. Except during the last year, when she had spells of confusion, particularly at night, I felt she enjoyed life. She loved to be taken out in her chair. Since her death, I have the wonderful feeling that I did all I could for her and she did not spend her last years, stuck in a Rest Home, unwanted.

My husband has had multiple sclerosis for 20 years and has been in a wheelchair for 15 years. One of the rewards we had was watching him learn to swim at 60 and win a gold medal.

Where else would he get one-to-one nursing? However irksome it is I know how best to keep him comfortable and one of the family.

It's not easy to cope but there is always a great comfort in knowing that one has done one's best. My wife has always loved her home and I shall try to keep her there until the end.

I have had to give up my sculpting work because of my bad back but I have started to draw. The drawings are gentle, about vulnerability and have come out of the business of caring.

It's knowing you have no conscience that you have neglected them. After physiotherapy in the first year, I was taught a few exercises to help David. Each time he could lift his arm a little higher and that was wonderfully rewarding. He was taught to wash and dress himself and each tiny little thing that a baby does naturally was an achievement – it gave you such a marvellous feeling.

I am lucky that my mother is very bright in spite of her handicaps, and her 'thank you' when I tuck her in bed (two to five times a night) makes up for everything.

What are the worries?

What nearly all carers talk about when they get together is the constant *worry* that never disappears: awake or asleep there are always nagging concerns about what is round the next corner. These are the kinds of difficulties carers live with every day:

- Living in a family with somebody suffering from a mental health problem can make you particularly anxiety-prone if the person's condition is very unpredictable. Many relatives of people diagnosed as schizophrenic describe it as 'living on the edge of a volcano'.
- Parents of children with learning difficulties never stop having to plan for the future: a particularly stressful time is when the child grows up and leaves school. There is often a lack of appropriate employment or day centre places for the young adult. The future looms large at this time and parents worry about how that person will manage when they are too old to continue caring.
- The absence of acceptable residential alternatives to home care is a real and constant worry for many carers who feel their own reserves are low.
- Carers who do not speak English as their first language may find help hard to find because of communication difficulties. Services may not be offered because of prevailing myths like 'Asian women can cope because of their extended families'.
- Medical advances mean that many children with life-threatening conditions live longer. Knowing your child will die but not knowing whether it will be one year or six adds to the daily strain of caring.
- Many people do not feel up to the practical demands of caring. Often carers are elderly themselves and find themselves having to lift, bathe and toilet their partner.

- Looking after someone with Alzheimer's disease means you have to be constantly on the look-out for that person's safety. They may wander out of the house or leave the gas on.
- Some carers have reason to fear for their own safety as some medical conditions (and some medication) can make a previously mild mannered person unpredictable and physically violent.
- Caring for a person with AIDS involves particular pressures for the carer, which may be made worse by other people's fears or prejudices. The illness itself can be unpredictable, and it can be hard to know how to respond to someone whose mood fluctuates between hope and despair.
- Looking after a partner who has developed multiple sclerosis in mid-life can suddenly change the balance of a relationship. Carers find they have to take on more and more of the running of the household in addition to the personal care of the partner.
- A teenager whose mother has terminal cancer may spend much of his or her out-of-school hours running errands or helping look after the parent. In addition to the pain of living alongside someone who is dying, the adolescent may also be practically held back from sharing in the same activities and education as their peers.

Describing carers as having problems or difficulties does not mean they regard the person they look after as 'the problem'. This common misunderstanding often makes carers reluctant to talk about their difficulties in case it should reflect badly on the person they look after.

More often than not, they want to carry on caring at home but need the proper advice, practical help and continuing support to do so. But carers do need help in managing and living with these situations, especially when there is no immediate way of taking away the problem.

All these situations are different, as are the solutions that can help. But, if you are a carer, you share something in common with all other carers. One word that keeps cropping up is 'unpredictable'. Part of the strain of caring is you just never know what will happen next. You do not know if the person you are looking after will make a sudden improvement or whether you will wake up in the middle of the night to a crisis.

Living under this kind of strain is exhausting. As nearly all caring situations are emotionally highly charged, it can be very difficult to see what would help when you are in the middle of it. But being clear with yourself about those aspects of caring you find most difficult is very important.

Recognising your own needs

Getting help for yourself *as well as* for the person you care for can ease the strain. It is often hard to see any point at which you became a carer if the situation has developed slowly. Or perhaps you simply don't describe yourself in this way. Parents of a child with disabilities may not see themselves as carers, only as parents. But there are additional strains to the parenting role which need to be taken into account.

It comes as a shock to many people to find that with a worsening medical condition, help does not automatically arrive in the home. There are some notable exceptions, and you may be very happy with the help you receive. But on the whole, the onus falls on you to ask for help in sharing the domestic and nursing tasks or to arrange a break from caring altogether.

This can be particularly hard to do because you may feel you are failing to cope or that it somehow shows you lack sufficient loving feelings. This is particularly the case for women, who often feel they *should* be able to cope because 'after all, he is my husband'. But love is not always enough. Everybody needs help to sustain care in the home and it is your right to ask for it.

If you can be clear about what would help you, professionals and people around you are more likely to respond. There are some very good schemes around that can give you a break or help you in other ways. How good the response to your request will be will vary enormously according to who you ask and where you live. But don't give up: keep on asking. Even if a service does not exist it should not stop you asking.

Remember, if you are a carer you are entitled to help. It is the responsibility of your local authority social services department to ensure that you and the person you look after receive a 'package of care' to help you in the home. You will find more details about this in chapter 8.

The next two chapters may help you understand the *effects* of caring on your life. This can be the first step in understanding what you, in your unique situation, might need to do to avoid ill health and exhaustion.

3 How caring can affect you

I soon realised I had to draw on everything I had learnt in life in order to cope and to plan for the future. But I knew too that if I was to survive these times I would have to be kind to myself.

Your experience of looking after a person who is ill or disabled will obviously depend on the degree of difficulty that person experiences in day-to-day living. But almost as important will be the quality of your relationship with that person *before* the onset of illness.

Taking on the personal care of another person is rarely a way of healing old wounds or repairing a stormy partnership. Caring at home can be intense, fraught and isolating. It can also be rewarding, enriching and satisfying – but generally only when you have plenty of practical support and encouragement. Even the most loving relationships can be sorely tested by the strain and difficulties imposed by chronic illness.

Many carers keep going in the knowledge that their efforts are sustaining a quality of life for their relative that would be hard to achieve in any other way. As Mary explained:

It's the satisfaction of knowing that my mother had some choices in the last few years of her life. That she was more in control of her life than she would have been in a home and I was able to provide things that she liked: jokes she liked, books she liked to read, to keep that side of her life going so that she was still herself – a very distinctive character.

As an afterthought, she added: 'I tell my children to put me in a home.' This is a sentiment often expressed by carers: 'I could not bear for my children to have to do what I did.' There is a powerful message here, and one that is a sad indictment of how people caring at home have been left to struggle alone without recognition or practical help.

The lack of acceptable alternatives to providing the care oneself is often the main reason why carers continue in their role long after they should, for their own sakes. Far from expecting reciprocal care from their own daughters and sons, many carers want to protect them from the personal cost of caring.

When a situation creeps up on you, such as a slowly evolving illness of a partner involving a long period of worry and uncertainty, it can be hard to remember how you felt before. So it sometimes takes a long hard look to realise that your feelings may be related to the strain of caring.

Are you exhausted?

Caring is strenuous and stressful. If you have been caring for some time and you feel you are not coping as well as you used to, it is not because you are a failure.

If you answer '*yes*' to these questions, the chances are you are suffering the effects of physical and emotional exhaustion:

Warning signs

- Do you wake up in the morning still feeling tired?
- Do you feel badly about yourself?
- Do you experience extreme 'highs' and 'lows' through the day?
- Do you feel like crying over trivial things?
- Do you have panic attacks or fits of anxiety about the future?
- Have you lost contact with close friends and/or family?
- Have you stopped enjoying sex?
- Do you use alcohol or drugs (such as sleeping pills or tranquillisers) excessively?
- Do you sometimes feel so exasperated you want to hit the person you look after?
- Are you being hit or otherwise hurt by the person you look after?
- Do you feel scared about becoming ill yourself?

If you recognise yourself there are two things you must do:

- stop blaming yourself
- find someone to talk to who understands

Easier said than done, I hear you say! But if you read on, you will see that many people who care for relatives at home experience very similar reactions and have found ways of overcoming them or making them more manageable. You may feel very alone, but there are many others out there who have experienced what you are living through.

Of course, everybody's situation is different and that is why there is never a single solution. Learning to recognise the traps and pitfalls can help. You may not be able to avoid them: if respite care in your area is poor, you will bear the brunt of this neglect. But it may help to know that you are missing a service you are entitled to receive.

Other things you may be able to change yourself. Many carers are very hard on themselves and have very high expectations of what they 'should' be able to do. But everyone has their limits, and if you are also in a situation which is distressing to you personally – perhaps someone close to you is suffering pain or no longer recognises you – then those limits will soon be reached. Bottling up unwelcome feelings is tiring; understanding and learning to live with complex and difficult feelings can ease your tiredness. You may recognise some of the emotions discussed in chapter 3.

Is being ill the only way to stop?

Although keeping a positive attitude is important, it is not self-indulgent to allow feelings of sadness, anger or helplessness. Sometimes people need to know that you are at a low ebb, otherwise you will get ill – like Doreen: 'I had so many people dependant on me that unless I was really ill I couldn't stop doing what I was doing so it had to be something dramatic. Like a slipped disc – or I had hepatitis one time.'

Common health problems for carers are often disabling conditions such as back pain and arthritis or stress-related illnesses such as asthma, migraine, insomnia and depression. Lack of sleep and physical exhaustion can mean there is just not enough energy to go around.

Even if you do not feel you can stop for your own sake, your body will probably make you! Often the reason people collapse is because they have not received the help they should have done: from the doctor, district nurse, social worker or whoever . . . But some carers feel driven to do absolutely everything they can until they are no longer able to do more. This is not necessarily serving the best interests of the person you look after. Indeed, it may be very distressing for that person to watch you being run into the ground.

Many carers feel they cannot afford to be ill: 'It plays on your mind all the time. It's a horrible thought. Even when I'm out, I think I must be careful crossing the road. I can't afford to have anything happen to me.' This may be a very real fear, especially if your own health is poor and you know the person you care for will be at risk if you do not return. One carer, Doug Drake, drew up his own identification card in case anything happened to him so that his wife, who suffers from Alzheimer's disease, would receive attention:

In the event of an accident:

I am a carer and I care for ....

Who is at..

She suffers from...............................and can't cope alone

Next of kin...

The reason so many carers suffer ill health is because they are carrying responsibilities that should not be shouldered alone. This is a national scandal, but one which is not likely to change overnight. In the meantime, it falls to you as a carer to learn how to set realistic limits for what you are prepared to do and to ask for help at every turn. You are saving the state money, so you have a right to ask for support.

4 Painful feelings

You don't want sympathy. You just want to talk it out of your system.

When carers get together, sooner or later they start to talk about the difficult feelings they are living with. Talking about it seems to help. The feelings may not go away, but hearing other people talk about the same things you have struggled with for weeks, or maybe years, can be reassuring. You may not be the kind of person who finds it easy to talk in this way, or you may prefer to keep these things private. That is, of course, your right.

Sometimes it helps to talk confidentially to a 'professional' who is trained to recognise psychological difficulties and help you to adjust to them (see page 21 for more information). But you do not need a professional to teach you how to talk: getting together with others in the same boat, it soon comes naturally.

You may not have the feelings discussed in the following pages. But, if you do, you are not unusual: emotional distress is a normal response in the fact of extreme and testing situations.

Guilt

Feelings of guilt underpin nearly all other feelings. Because they are so much a part of carers' experience, guilt crops up in all kinds of ways. This is largely because of a wider lack of recognition about the physical work that is involved in caring at home which places unrealistic expectations on carers. Because caring is considered to be 'women's work', it also suffers from the devaluation of all activities that are considered to be 'natural' for women. Men who are carers suffer from this lack of recognition too, just as men who choose a caring profession such as nursing must accept the same conditions as women.

Here are some of the things that can trigger feeling guilty:

- You may feel you are not good enough in your role as carer because you have conflicting demands made on you.
- You may have unrealistically high expectations of what you, as a carer, can do.
- You may want to make up for past disagreements if your previous relationship was difficult. But caring for someone to compensate for the past causes problems for you both unless you can reach a new understanding.
- Recognising any of the feelings described in this chapter may provoke guilt because you may feel it is a betrayal of the person you care for.

Guilt feelings are a trap because they can keep you stuck in a situation that may not be good for you, the person you look after or your family.

Caring from a sense of guilt can make it hard to plan rationally for the future or to accept any help.

Introducing three carers

It is often helpful to hear others voice those thoughts you have kept to yourself. Nothing substitutes for doing this yourself, but on the following pages you can be a 'fly on the wall' while three carers discuss some of their feelings about caring at home.

Helen Armstrong, Lola Frost and Edie Badiali met at the Carers' Centre in Hove, East Sussex and very kindly allowed me to tape and print their discussion.

In brief, these are their stories:

My name is Edie. My daughter was left brain-damaged after a whooping cough injection and from then on she's had severe epilepsy and was left mentally handicapped. That was 23 years ago. I have also looked after my mother and my father. My father suffered severe heart trouble which left my mum on her own. She had cancer, so I was running her home as well as looking after Suzy.

I'm Lola. My husband had a stroke in 1983 and for 5 years, I cared for him. After his first stroke, I had heart trouble, which made it twice as difficult. Three years after the first stroke he had another severe one and also developed

Alzheimer's Disease. His last two years were very, very
hard for both of us. He was completely helpless, had to
have everything done for him. He was doubly incontinent.
He was able to walk, but apart from that he had no means
of looking after himself.

I am Helen. My mother became more dependent on me as
she got older and when my youngest child was born, my
father died. Then I took over responsibility for her. She
suffered from bad bouts of depression and she also had
arthritis. Eventually when she died she had cancer. But the
cancer was never a problem, it was the depression that
really made her suffer.

Anxiety and fear

Do you feel like you are 'constantly on a knife edge', like you
are 'living on your nerves'. Do you get headaches, stomach
upsets, palpitations or panic attacks? If you do not know what
the future holds you will probably feel worried and frightened.
This is understandable and often a direct consequence of bad or
absent services in the local community.

This is how our three carers experienced these feelings:

Edie

I get terrible anxiety and I can hardly control it. It just piles into me.
I'm very emotionally involved with Suzy and I'm worried about her
future the whole of the time. I've taught myself how to cope, as I've
got older. I can recognise the signs when I'm 'going under' again.
These are the times when I will arrange things so that I can sit very
quietly for a day or two. I used to feel very guilty if I was thinking
about myself, but now I make those 'my days' and I keep them
absolutely clear and that is the only way I can get over that feeling of
'going under'.

What would be your advice to other carers who are getting into
a similar situation?

Edie

I think they need to go to their doctor because there are counsellors
around and I found that very useful. If you don't go to a counsellor, try
to find someone you can really talk to . . .

Lola

Yes, I agree. I'm talking after the event as it were, because I'm on my own now. But for the first couple of years I had nobody: you cannot talk to family or to friends. It's not that they don't want to know but it's easier with an outsider who understands. I found a stroke club and the carers formed a group that met once a month while our partners were in another room. That session once a month was a lifeline because you were with people in similar circumstances and there were no inhibitions at all. It is so necessary to get yourself in touch with somebody in a similar situation.

Edie

You don't want sympathy. You just want to talk it out of your system. I could just rattle on every day. Nobody can actually do anything – they can give you practical help but what I find hard is the emotional part. It's got to be the right person, of course.

Anger

The most usual and, for many people, the most frightening feeling is anger. If you have very high expectations of being patient and loving every second of the day, it can be upsetting to feel angry and frustrated. But feeling guilty about it will not help – that simply turns the anger on yourself and sooner or later you will start to feel depressed.

Carers have every reason to feel angry and resentful if they are left to cope alone. You may feel tied and trapped by caring and angry at the opportunities you have missed.

Anger may also be a reaction to loss – witnessing the suffering of someone you are close to can make you feel angry at the injustice of it all. Or it may be a reaction to the anger expressed by the person you look after: carers often bear the brunt of that anger and frustration.

This is what the carers had to say:

Edie

I very rarely lose my temper but holding it back is emotionally tiring. I do feel very annoyed with Suzy, but I don't feel guilty any more because I can see she's winding me up. I couldn't see it before and used to think it was all me. That has taken a lot of that awful stress feeling away.

How do you show your anger?

Edie

I've stamped the floor really hard, or brought my fist down on something. Now, I don't get it so badly because I'm accepting it and I don't get so churned up.

Lola

I used to shout back at Victor. I got past the stage of dissolving into tears – you get to the stage there's no tears left. You're just angry. Angry because he is suffering far more than I am. I used to go out and walk round the garden or knock the pots and pans about in the kitchen. By the time I've done that, he would have got over his violent mood . . .

Helen

I used to go out and kick the back wall in the yard – it was about the only thing that wouldn't suffer if it was kicked!

Lola

No wonder you've got a bad foot! You have to laugh, don't you? It's very important to get together with someone in the same circumstances and have a laugh . . .

Sadness

Feeling of sadness are often hard to express because you may feel you have to hide them from the person you care for. You may feel very helpless: 'I'd sometimes just cry because I wanted to do something and I knew there was no way I could make her better.' One way people cope with grief is to try to avoid the pain by keeping very busy. This may help in the short term but is likely to make you very tired because your energy will also be used in keeping your feelings at a distance.

As the carers say:

Helen

It's like you're protecting everybody; your family, the person you look after . . . but nobody's protecting you. You just have to keep going.

Lola

You can't be natural can you? You've got to lie and put up a false front all the time . . .

Helen

Yes, it's this ridiculous cheerfulness all the time . . .

Edie

When you're feeling like crying inside because you know what's happening to them . . . you know you're going to lose them . . .

Helen

And you'd like to talk to them about what it feels like . . .

Edie

I know, my mum was in the most dreadful pain, but she wasn't going to say much to me about it . . . but I could see it.

Loneliness

The strain of caring can mean you lose touch with people and are not able to maintain a social life. If your partner is ill, you will be coping with the loss of that relationship and possibly the loss of emotional support and sexual intimacy. You may feel very alone. The insensitivity of others may make you feel like 'the person in the shadows' or as Helen said, 'I was just the person who answered the door.'

The three carers were asked whether they cared alone. This is what they said:

Edie

I had my husband: he helped . . . a bit. Apart from that, I had no outside help.

Lola

I had family, in-laws. No one to help with day-to-day caring. I did have a supportive doctor who looked after us very well. For the first two years I had no nursing help, no carers to contact. I didn't know where to get help for benefits or anything. Nobody told me.

Edie

I've always tried to be involved with things that were going on, but I found I was stopping even getting involved with people. It was all too much. The worry with Suzy was enough without having anything else on top of it. I was beginning to be on my own all the time.

Helen

You survive by narrowing your interests and lowering your expectations and just getting by. You can't torment yourself with things you'd like to be doing.

Lola

Yes, you live from day to day.

Doesn't there come a point where it gets too narrow?

Edie

Yes, but it was the only way I could cope. It took me a year to get down here [the Carers' Centre]. I'm very glad I did.

Lola

I'm celebrating today: I've passed a great milestone. I developed a phobia where I could not go out alone, but last Monday I walked from the town hall to here on my own. That's the first time I've walked alone in the street for three and a half years.

Finding someone to talk to

If you feel it would help to talk things over with someone beyond your immediate family or friends, you might want to consider these ideas.

Joining a group

There are all kinds of organisations that offer advice, information and support for people with particular illnesses or disabilities and their families. Some of them may run support groups specifically for carers. If you have a council for voluntary service or a volunteer bureau in your area, they should be able to put you in touch. If you live in the country, try the rural community council.

Sometimes groups are run by the social services department or are attached to a hospital. The Carers National Association can tell you if they have a branch near you (see page 130). If you are caring for someone under 19, you may prefer to find a parents' support group by getting in touch with Contact a Family (see page 130).

Many groups arrange help for the person you care for so that you are free to attend a meeting. You may feel, though, that you do not want to attend meetings; don't let that put you off

contacting a group – it is still worthwhile because they may
have a newsletter or know of other services that could be useful
to you. Alternatively, you might want to arrange to meet
someone from the group in a more informal way for a chat.
(For more information about voluntary organisations and
groups, see chapter 9.)

Counselling

You do not have to be 'mad' or 'neurotic' to benefit from
counselling. If you are coping with complex problems you may
need someone to help you see a way through them. One of the
advantages of counselling is that it is completely confidential so
you can have the chance to talk through feelings or problems
that may be hard to share with friends or relatives.

If you are feeling trapped by your situation and feel you are
going round in circles trying to sort it out, a counsellor will
listen to you and might help you find some alternatives that
you have not thought of.

Counselling is a fairly young profession and counsellors
themselves vary in skill, approach and training. You will want to
select someone who is knowledgeable about the stresses of
caring at home and it is usual to have a first meeting where you
can find out about the counsellor and decide if you want to
work together. There will be a number of questions you need to
ask before you commit yourself such as:

- What training/approach does the counsellor use? If this
  means nothing to you, ask for some examples of what this
  means in practice.
- How much does s/he charge?
- What is the commitment on both sides – i.e. how many
  sessions, for how long?
- Do you have to pay for sessions you cannot attend?
- Finally, you need to ask yourself whether you feel
  comfortable to work with this person. Heed your instincts.

It is not easy to get counselling on the NHS, but it is
becoming more usual. You will need to be referred by your
doctor. The best way to get in touch with a counsellor is often
the personal recommendation of someone you trust. The
counselling service of a local college or university will usually
know of reputable counsellors who work freelance.

Counsellors can charge anything between £5 and £25 an
hour: some operate a sliding scale for people on a low income
and a few offer a free service.

The following organisations can suggest names and addresses
of private counsellors or therapists in your area. They may be
able to advise on low-cost counselling for people on low
incomes: the British Association for Counselling, the British
Association of Psychotherapists and the Women's Therapy
Centre (see pages 130–3).

Helplines

Most of the national voluntary organisations listed on pages
129–41 offer an advice and welfare service and may be able to
put you in touch with local members. There are also a few
national helplines which operate on low rates or are free:

- *Cancer*. If you care for someone with cancer, call freephone
  0800-181199 run by BACUP (British Association of Cancer
  United Patients) to speak to a trained cancer nurse who can
  give information and emotional support to carers or to
  patients.
- *AIDS*. A free national advice service on HIV/AIDS is available
  on 0800-567123.
- *Epilepsy*. The British Epilepsy Association runs a helpline on
  0345-089599 (9.00-4.30 Mon-Thurs, 9.00-4.00 Fri); this
  number can be dialled anywhere in the UK for local rates.

Don't forget, you can also call the carers' adviser at the Carers
National Association on 071-724-7776 (normal telephone rates
apply).

Finding your own outlet

As with all suggestions in this book, these are made for you to
use if they fit – and ignore if they do not. No answer is right for
everybody and you may be the kind of person who prefers to
keep your feelings to yourself. They will still need some outlet,
though, and there are other ways to channel feelings: through
drawing, writing or, as Mr Harris describes, through physical
activity:

Sometimes I feel depressed about the kind of life I have as a carer.
Sometimes I feel very tired. Sometimes I feel very unhappy about what
my wife has to endure as a result of her stroke. Sometimes all three of
these feelings descend on me at the same time. When this happened
last month, I went out into the garden and did a couple of hours' hard
work. I hate gardening and, at 70 years of age, I am not all that fond of
manual work. But, as I put the tools away and went into the house, I
suddenly realised I was whistling. I was ready to face life again.

5 How you can help yourself

When my wife suffered a severe stroke, people would ask about her and then they would ask about me. This was the means by which I came to realise that if I was to care for my wife, I must myself remain physically and mentally healthy.

I decided that some part of every day would be reserved for my own personal activities so that I could, for a short time, forget about my wife and our common problems.

Many carers' problems actually stem from their strengths: qualities of sensitivity, empathy and compassion. Caring about a person means a willingness and an ability to understand the feelings and needs of another. It is this ability to empathise that makes it so hard for people who become carers. Often the decision to care for someone is made in the full knowledge that it will mean making some sacrifices and that it may bring personal hardship to the carer. Christine explains:

At the start of an illness, people are still very much themselves with their own standards of what they like and don't like. You have to consider their dignity and feelings. They don't want to be put together with people who are nothing like them. You need to respect that. Their decisions count for an awful lot. The decisions we made were to fit in with my mothers' needs.

Juggling your own needs and those of an infirm or disabled relative is hard work and you need help. Putting someone else's needs before your own may feel like an expression of love in the short term, but over a long time resentment can set in: 'When Mother came to live here, I had no intention of changing my life – I still don't see why I should; but gradually things have had to be given up.'

Unfortunately the things that are given up first are often the very things that sustain your own mental and physical health. This is a constant struggle but there are some things you can do that will help.

Check your 'safety net'

So how do you go about getting the support you need? The first stage is recognising what you in your unique situation will need – both now and in the foreseeable future. While everybody's list will be different in detail, you are almost certainly likely to run into trouble if you do not have (or know how to get) any of the following:

- breaks from caring: both regular time off during the week and blocks of time if you are caring over months or years
- someone to talk to who understands and recognises your situation
- information and advice about benefits, services, legal rights
- medical advice about the illness or condition of the person you care for
- practical help in the home: nursing, lifting, shopping
- opportunities to meet other people in the same situation
- someone to call in an emergency
- other interests/employment

This checklist is your 'safety net'. If you know how to go about finding these things, you may be more prepared for the future.
    Make a note of the things that are missing:

I need information about how to find ....
....

Keep up your contacts with people

It is important to know what help is available from the beginning because then you can make plans to take it up if you need it. But sometimes things develop at a pace you do not expect – a crisis may creep up on you or happen out of the blue – and you are locked into coping from day to day. So it is not only information you need to know you can rely on, but *people* too.

If you are in employment, you may need to talk to your employer. If you are concerned about not receiving a sympathetic hearing, find out what your rights are from your union or welfare officer. Some employers recognise the need to allow family leave during illness and are in any case more likely to be helpful if they are kept informed. The costs of caring are often very high and a personal visit to get the bank manager on your side might also be a wise move.

People differ in their needs for a social life, but to avoid that 'narrowing down' of contacts described in the last chapter you might want to actively seek out people you can trust. The more people you can turn to, the less you will feel you are leaning too much on one or two people.

You may feel you don't want to show people the strain you are under, or perhaps the person you care for prefers to 'keep it in the family'. That is understandable, but things are more likely to become difficult if you cannot confide in someone who knows you and your situation.

Do you have someone:

- who can give you important information you need?
- who makes you feel competent and of value?
- to whom you feel close?
- with whom you can discuss concerns or worries?
- upon whom you can depend in a crisis?
- with whom you can share good or bad news?
- who will be honest with you and challenge you?
- who will help you out with daily routines?

Not many people are lucky enough to have all of these, but if you cannot answer 'yes' to any at all, try and find out if there is a carers' group in your area. If you do not know where to start locally, then contact the Carers National Association. If you care for someone under the age of 19, get in touch with Contact a Family or see pages 129–41 for other addresses that may be helpful.

If it helps, make a note to yourself:

I need to make contact with someone who can ....
....

Identify what causes you stress

The next thing you can do is learn to recognise the situations most likely to cause stress. These are different for everybody: one person will be quite prepared to deal with incontinence but may find lack of communication very distressing. For another person, it may be the competing demands of small children and elderly parents. By becoming aware of what *you* find difficult you are more likely to find help. The situation may seem insoluble, but if you can describe it clearly to other people they may be able to help you.

Here are some examples. You may have others.

My source of stress is . . .

- not knowing for how long I am going to be giving home care
- having had the decision of caring forced on me rather than having freely chosen it
- being of advanced age or having ill-health myself
- not having the training or information I need to provide care
- lack of free time for myself
- loss of freedom
- changes in family life
- family conflicts
- competing demands between my role as a carer and other roles in my life.
- loss of social contacts and social life
- feelings of guilt
- financial losses or difficulties
- having to carry out tasks I find unpleasant or embarrassing
- changes in the personality of the person I care for
- lack of sleep
- needing a complete break from caring

(Material adapted from *Carers: You Matter Too!*, prepared for the National Council for the Aged, Dublin, by Prof. Joyce O'Connor and Dr Helen Ruddle.)

What are the warning signs when things are getting too much for you? Some people have physical symptons: rashes, allergies, headaches, stomach upsets – all these symptoms are *real*. A stress-related symptom is not imaginary: do not dismiss it as 'just stress' because it is the body's way of protesting. Left unheeded, the body will soon find other ways of making its point which could mean days or years of illness.

Sometimes the signs are more personal to you – but *you*

know what they mean. You may find yourself getting very
irritable, forgetful or you may feel overwhelmed and helpless.
Take a few moments now to think about this and jot down a
few notes for yourself:

My own source of stress is ....

....

My own warning signs are ....

....

Look after your own needs

'It's easy to say think of yourself – but you don't. You think of
the other person 24 hours a day.'

Your concern for the person you look after may occupy your
thoughts and your time day and night. But it is important to get
into the habit of making time for yourself, even if it is only for
short periods. The people who manage to keep body and soul
together while caring do seem to share that ability to 'switch
off': one carer describes it as 'being able to go off on a different
plane'.

Part of the battle is already won if you recognise how
important it is to look after yourself. It is likely that your own
needs are far down on that endless mental list of things to do.
But if you have got as far as reading this, you are well on the
way. Here are some ideas you might try:

- *Treat yourself.* Think of something you would enjoy – it
  doesn't have to be anything unusual. Perhaps listening to
  your favourite music, watching television or doing a
  crossword. Take a long hot bath: a few drops of lavender oil
  will calm and relax you; basil or rosemary oil will perk you
  up. You may want to go out for an evening, go to the pub or
  meet a friend for lunch. Other people prefer to be on their
  own, take a walk in the country or go for a swim – or
  sometimes just sit and do nothing. The effort of making
  arrangements to have time for yourself can make it seem not
  worth the bother, but if you can build these times into your
  week you will soon wonder how you managed without them.
- *Check you are getting all the help you can.* You may find there
  are ways you can ease the strain by reading through Part II
  and checking your local sources of help. Your own situation

will change with time, so it is worth sitting down every so
often and reviewing the situation. Let yourself leave non-
essential work until you have more stamina.

● *Check you are eating properly.* This is an obvious but essential
point. It is easy to neglect your diet if your day is full of
somebody else's routine.

● *Find a way to take exercise.* If your day does not permit you to
go swimming or take other vigorous exercise, could you do
something more gentle such as gardening, going for a walk
or a few stretching exercises at home?

● *Do you have a means of relaxation?* Relaxation is something that
can be learnt and practised in odd moments through the day.
Try this simple exercise and practise it when you can:

  • Sit comfortably on a chair or on a cushion on the floor
  with your hands at rest, palms facing upwards.

  • Be aware of how you are breathing and concentrate on
  breathing slowly and deeply. Don't force it. Let it
  happen gradually.

  • Focus your attention on your weight resting on the chair
  or floor and of your spine lengthening and straightening
  right up to the back of your neck. Feel your head
  moving slightly forwards and upwards from the crown.

  • If thoughts or anxieties keep coming into your mind,
  just let them be there. As you breathe out, imagine you
  are letting them go, one by one.

  • Do the same with tension in your body. Be aware of any
  aches or pains. As you breathe out imagine you are
  letting them go. Each one may take several breaths.

  • Imagine yourself in a favourite place which is peaceful:
  it could be a place you know or an imaginary scene.
  Explore the place in your mind's eye: notice the colours,
  the smells, the scenery. This is a place you can return to
  any time you need to.

  • When you feel ready, become aware again of your body
  resting on the floor or in the chair.

  • With each inward breath, imagine you are taking in new
  life and energy and with each breath out, you are
  releasing tension and anxiety.

  • Slowly open your eyes and sit quietly for a few
  moments.

● *Finally – get some unbroken sleep.* Often, the most difficult one
to arrange, but if you are able to get some time off, try to
treat this as a priority rather than rushing to get other things
done while you have the time. There's no time like the
present, so promise yourself at least one treat this week.

> I promise myself I shall ....
> ....

Let some things go

It upsets me seeing Dorothy getting so tired since I had the stroke. I tell her to sit down and not bother with a cooked meal tonight. It makes me feel such a burden.

Sometimes it is better to drop your standards. The person you care for will understand if you are able to talk together. It may be more important for your relationship together to allow that person to be able to show concern for *you*.

Even if you are not able to talk about these things, you will find it easier to manage if you can let things go. As Kathleen says, 'You have to hang on to your sense of humour at all costs. I wish I had realised earlier that a very tidy home wasn't important, something broken here and there doesn't matter. People are more important than things.'

If you can snatch time away from caring or domestic chores, treat it as precious. This is *your* time and you need it to catch up on sleep or just to maintain your own interests. You may be tempted to 'spring clean' the house but stop to think first whether this is number one priority.

> What are the things that you can let go of when you are under strain? Jot them down now:
> ....
> ....
> ....

Learn the art of self-protection

You are not being selfish if you feel you need time to yourself. Call it self-protection, but you may have to be prepared to persuade others to give you the help you need.

People who care at home do not want to be seen as saintly Florence Nightingales. However, the reality is that many people will be only too willing to believe you have superhuman qualities that sustain you throughout the day and night.

Busy professionals may genuinely want to help but are often working with few resources; they may feel embarrassed by the lack of help they are able to offer. It may seem to you that they do not wish to hear that you need someone to keep an eye on your parent once a week while you go to the shops. Family members may conceal from themselves how much work you are doing and can underplay the strain you are under.

This behaviour stems from other people's sense of guilt that they are not doing enough, but it will probably make *you* feel guilty unless you recognise it. These attitudes can make you feel as if you are wrong to tell people when things are difficult for you. It can make you feel guilty for complaining about being tired, needing a break or time to do things that you enjoy. Or you may feel that you have been disloyal to the person you look after for saying anything at all.

Take a look at some of the notes you have made. Do any of these things seem unreasonable? The answer is probably no. Keep on believing you have a right to your own life, your own time. It does not mean you care for your relative or partner any less. If you feel very resistant to asking for help, look at the next chapter and see if you recognise any of the situations described there. If you do not have any difficulty in this area, skip this section and use Part II to see if you are getting the services you are entitled to.

6 Asking for help

Does asking for help mean you are failing to cope? The short answer is 'no' and you probably know this. The way you *feel* can be very different because of a combination of your own and other people's expectations. Here are a few reasons that carers have identified.

'Other people expect me to be able to cope'

When Margaret's mother was taken into hospital, Margaret was already looking after her father who had bowel cancer as well as her husband and three children. Because her ability to cope was never questioned, it was almost impossible for her to challenge those assumptions.

Because I was *there*, I was expected to take over. Nobody asked me if I could cope. I didn't feel up to the responsibility, but it was expected of me. I had the feeling of letting everyone down. I am 40 and people expect me to have more physical stamina that I have, especially since I damaged my back catching my mother when she fell.

Obviously this was bad practice on the part of the hospital (and the GP who was also involved) – but the result was that Margaret felt that it was *her* inadequacy. At a time of crisis, it is hard to find the energy to fathom out the best way to deal with a situation such as this and it often takes someone close to you who is not so emotionally involved to point out what is happening.

Try not to be pressured into decisions you are uncomfortable with. It may be easier to do this if you have a friend with you, or someone from a local voluntary organisation who can act as your 'advocate'; in other words, speak on your behalf or back

you up in your demands. Alternatively, ask to speak to the
hospital social worker to talk through the possible options.

'Keep it in the family'

The wish to try to maintain care in the home is often 'to keep
everything as normal as possible'. This may involve keeping up
a front to friends, neighbours and even family in order to
preserve the dignity of the person being looked after.

Complaining about your situation can feel as if you are
rejecting or letting down the person you look after, so there is a
temptation to underplay difficulties for fear of upsetting that
person. 'It's not as bad as all that' or 'It's far worse for him of
course, I don't have the pain to deal with.' But sometimes this
competent and coping exterior can work against the carer. Mrs
Day explains:

At one time I would not talk of private matters to anyone outside the
family. I would not be disloyal in revealing difficult traits or situations
– but I have *had* to have that release and have *had* to let barriers down
and I find – maybe I am fortunate – folk are not awful gossips but are
most understanding and helpful.

In the area where Mrs Day lives, the local social services team
has a worker whose sole responsibility is to work with carers.
Mrs Day's own experience was a very positive one: 'Through
social services I received ready provision of practical help about
the home; and because of their kindly and sympathetic words, I
know that I can go to them for help at any time even if it is just
to discuss things.'

'I tried to get help but they said there wasn't any!'

Unfortunately Mrs Day's description is not the one many carers
report. All too often, having plucked up the courage to ask for
help, the response is discouraging. Do not take this as the last
word on the matter. As Eric says: 'I had to negotiate for a while
before I got what I wanted, so that is an important point. Do not
take 'no' for an answer without a struggle.'

By the time you read this, the new community care legislation
should be in place, which means that local authority social
service departments are required to organise care in the home.
This clarifies where you should go, but change may be slow.

Professional people are not deliberately keeping information
or help from you. They may genuinely wish to help but feel

powerless to do so. Working with carers means confronting one's own fears about death, terminal illness, attitudes to disability, illness without cure. Professional training does not always equip people to do this.

Doctors are trained to base most of their practice on 'curing' people. One doctor said that when he made home visits, he rarely asked the carer how he or she was feeling because he feared 'opening up a Pandora's box'. This reveals more about his own difficulties in dealing with people's emotions than a realistic appraisal of what he could offer. For many carers, simply knowing that their doctor is maintaining a watchful eye is enough.

There is no excuse for an unhelpful reception to your request, but it does not mean your query was wrong or stupid or that you do not deserve help. There may be reasons why the professional workers do not respond in the way you want:

- They may not know how to respond to a general plea for help: the more specific the request, the easier it is to say where to find the answer.
- They may not recognise *your* need for support. Some workers will only recognise the person you look after as the client or patient.
- They may be under pressure, lacking in resources and unsupported themselves. Often this means people do not think creatively about other help that may be available through voluntary organisations or other channels.
- They may not respond quickly to a request because they are short of time and already have more people on their books than they can manage.

If you find your social worker or other professional people are not helpful, do at least keep up your contact with them. Staff changes happen quite regularly in some agencies and may bring a more sympathetic person. Finding out about what services are available can be hard work, but you can help yourself by:

- Being as clear as you can about your problem: jot down a few notes before you call. It may not always be possible to know what action you want taken, but it might help to think this through.
- If the person you talk to is not able to help, try to find out who else you should talk to, to get the answer you need. Ask for the telephone number or address.

Sometimes, the plain fact is that help does not come. Services are not offered and you are left on your own. If this is your situation, find ways to make formal complaints (see chapter 11). Write to your MP, involve the media. Do whatever you can to make your complaint public: the Carers National Association can advise you further.

'We didn't know who to ask'

It is unfortunately often still the case that at the moment you most need information and advice there appears to be no one to turn to. This is particularly true for many parents who learn of the birth of a child with special needs. One parent carer relates how she heard the consultant tell her that her child had been born with severe brain damage as she was coming round from a caesarean section. No counselling or support was offered.

The way in which you are given a diagnosis of severe handicap will obviously affect the way you feel about asking for further help, leaving you mistrustful of professionals and reluctant to turn to them for advice. A traumatic experience such as this can affect you profoundly, to the extent that you feel as if you are re-living the experience of that realisation every time you ask for help.

If this is your experience, do try and contact a parents' support group. Other people in a similar position can understand your feelings and will be able to give you anecdotal information about who is helpful, where to go to get information and so on . . . National and local voluntary organisations can clarify information if you are confused by what your specialist or doctor is telling you. Services do vary a great deal between different authorities and some parent carers have even decided to move house or flat in order to be able to use better services.

'We've never needed help before. We'll get by'

A fierce wish to preserve independence is often tied to a fear that accepting help will pass control for decisions into someone else's hands. Joan's mother has been disabled since an accident when Joan was 9 years old. She is now 54 and cares for both her parents who both require round-the-clock attention. Joan prefers to manage with the minimum of help and is reluctant to ask for any. She says, 'I would be bothered that my parents would be upset. You see it might be a slippery slope. I might put something in motion that would run away and the decisions would no longer be mine.' The statutory services do not have the right to take away the person you look after or to do anything without your agreement or the persmission of the person you care for. However, this can only happen in the unlikely case of neglect or the (more likely) case that you yourself break down under the strain. Ironically, this outcome is much more likely if you *do not* get help in time. If things have to reach a crisis before help is acceptable, then someone else will have to step in.

Wanting to guard personal details about your situation is a natural concern, but sometimes this has to be put to one side. Winifred describes how she felt:

I found literature at the doctor's surgery and plucked up courage to call the carers' worker at social services. It was very difficult at first. In asking for help I disclosed things I know my husband wouldn't approve of, but I knew I was under a lot of mental strain and needed help. I now have a 'sitter' to look after him while I do the shopping and one complete day of freedom when he goes to day care.

Sometimes the person you care for may refuse to have strangers in the house or may be upset that the routine is being changed by going to a day centre. Often another person whom your relative respects can be more persuasive than you – for example, the family doctor, social worker or a close friend.

Another concern is that nobody else can offer the quality of care that you can. This may be true but there are ways to make it easier: for example, by gradual introduction to alternative care (also, see chapter 12 for tips on passing on information about a daily routine to a helper). If you have serious concerns about the quality of care you might wish to make a formal complaint (see chapter 11).

Living from day to day is often the only way to cope, but if you are denying there is a problem you will probably feel worried about the future. As Joan said, 'I'm talking from a situation I can manage. But I'm growing older and who will look after me?'

'He can't manage without me. I have to do everything.'

Help does not always have to come from outside the household. In some instances, you may be able to ask more from the person you look after. However ill or disabled the person you care for, there will still be things that person has control over. You do not have to take responsibility for all the problems that person has.

Of course, there are exceptions in this: someone suffering from Alzheimer's disease is not able to use the inhibiting mechanism that regulates ordinary behaviour. Looking after someone with senile dementia means you cannot expect the same 'give and take' as in other relationships, which is one reason why it can be a particularly draining condition to live with. But with many other conditions it is important to continue to negotiate about how much the person you look after can do for him or herself. You will both continue to have social, emotional and intellectual needs which are independent of your relationship. By devoting yourself exclusively to caring, the other person can start to feel a burden and lose a sense of purpose. One carer explains: 'Having one's independence taken away is a real blow. Most problems are caused by his frustration. We sometimes quarrel but always try to talk about it afterwards.'

A person who is physically dependent can feel all power and control is taken away. This is when apathy and depression can set in. Creating a lifestyle that continues to make reasonable demands on a person who is dependent in many practical ways can redress the balance and will help to make you both happier. It is a way of respecting that person's independence and ability to make decisions.

'I'm not the sort of person to yell for help'

Are you the sort of person that always provides the shoulder to cry on? Do you like people to think of you as strong and dependable? If so, you are probably not accustomed to asking for help yourself.

But none of us are able to be entirely independent, and if you have special demands on you, you need to rely on others for support. If it is hard for you to ask for that from friends or relatives, try to think how you feel when people ask *you* for help. Do you despise them for it, or do you feel touched? Habits of a lifetime die hard, but unusual circumstances may demand unusual behaviour.

You may feel worried that you will not be able to repay favours from friends, but there may be ways you have not thought of. If you are at home much of the time, it may be helpful to a friend living close by that you can keep an eye on their flat or perhaps you can take phone calls for them. Some people will be happy to help and will enjoy the sense of being involved and useful without expecting anything in return. They may even be relieved to discover you are not superhuman!

Perhaps you think there are others worse off than you. There always are, but that is not a reason to feel you are not entitled to statutory help. Social services and community nursing are not only for people who are really desperate. In fact, the more services you use, the more likely they are to be available to other people. For example, a 'sitting service' that is under-used is much more vulnerable to being cut in the next year's budget than one that is able to demonstrate regular take-up. They are services you are entitled to use to maintain a reasonable quality of life for you and the person you look after as an alternative to residential care.

'People have always cared for their relatives. I should be able to cope alone'

It can be very distressing for the person you look after to see *you* under strain. As Pat explains:

My husband has a full-time job as an accountant. His mother has recently had a stroke and I have MS. I can walk with a frame but my legs are getting weak and I'm apt to fall and strain muscles. I cannot get to the loo so he has to carry me, wash out soiled clothes, change incontinence pads . . . He needs a rest and a break from our four walls.

The current emphasis on 'community care' has meant that families often carry a heavy load. The community care policy has meant that big institutions and long-stay hospitals have been closed in favour of people being cared for in their own homes.

This sounds humane and forward-looking. The reality has been a shambles. Most people agree that the large institutions were not an appropriate way to look after people in need of care. But people from all parties and all sections of the community have criticised this government's failure to set up alternative support for vulnerable members of society and their carers.

This failure has meant that families, and especially women, have taken on a large part of the care. It has also meant that people, who are not fortunate in having close family to turn to, have left hospital with little or no support.

Your local authority social services department has a

responsibility to co-ordinate services to assist you in caring at home – either by providing a service themselves or contracting a private or voluntary organisation to do so. So keep asking!

Part II
How to Find Help

7 Looking at your needs

What information do you need if you are considering taking on the care of a relative?

Taking on the care of a relative very often happens in a time of crisis with little opportunity to think through the consequences, but if you *are* able to plan ahead, these are some of the important questions to get sorted out as soon as you can. The first question is the most important and you need to return to it when you have answered the others. You will probably feel under some pressure to answer 'yes', but saying 'no' can often be the right answer for you *and* for the person who needs care. It does not mean you do not love the person: on the contrary it can mean that you are honest enough to know that he or she would benefit more by making alternative caring arrangements.

- Am I the right person to do this?
- What are the alternatives?
- How long is the care likely to go on for?
- Where will my relative live?
- What are her/his wishes?
- What financial help will I get?
- What care is likely to be needed? (List in detail. It is important to be practical at this stage – do not underestimate the practical tasks involved)
- How much can I do? What are my limits?
- What help will I get?
- How will the rest of the family be involved?
- How will I get time off?

You will probably want to talk these questions through with

family, a close friend or partner and the person who needs the care. Try to meet with someone who is already caring to talk about what help is available in your area, or contact a local carers' group or organisation. Once you are clear in your own mind you will need to talk to your doctor or hospital specialist and you should also contact your local social services department.

As far as is possible, establish a system of shared care with other relatives. Try to be clear about what you can and cannot do and ensure that the responsibility is equally shared.

Kate's story – or how to care for an elderly mother-in-law and survive!

When Kate's mother-in-law fell and broke her leg, Kate and the family had four weeks in which to consider 'what to do about Granny'. She was 70 and would be coming out of hospital with a plaster cast that would remain on for several months. They decided to offer to have her in their home and this is where she stayed until she was ready to return to her own upstairs flat.

Kate: It was a joint decision. My husband and I talked about how it had felt the last time she came to stay – when she came for one week and stayed for two! I had a good relationship with her and I didn't want to lose that. We also talked about it with the boys. They like Granny – but it was they who were going to lose playing space. We decided she would have to stay upstairs. That way she would be near the toilet but also it would mean we wouldn't be 'taken over'. Next we asked the hospital 'What will we need? What do you have that we haven't got that makes life easier – rails, frames, etc – to allow Granny to get from her room to the toilet?' We measured up and arrived at a solution that wouldn't be too inconvenient for our small boys. Then we said to her, 'Would you like to come to us?'

Interviewer: So you did some forward planning and you looked at the problems and everyone's needs.

Kate: Yes, we looked on the black side – assumed it would be at least 6 months. We made a list of all the things that would have to be done – breakfast, cups of tea, washing her, taking her to the toilet – all through the day. Feeling that I'm entitled to my needs as well was very necessary. Looking after yourself is as important as anything else – it's no good if you fall apart. I knew I couldn't lift her – she's bigger than me – and I stuck to my Saturday morning lie-in, so I didn't give up everything. Things like that. We also said 'We think it would be fair if you gave us xx a week' – for food plus a bit more to cover the fact that we'll need to go out a bit more to cope with the extra strain. It's like with a new baby, you can easily let it take over completely.

Interviewer: How did you feel about caring?

Kate: It wasn't the practicalities which were real work. You feel so terribly responsible for somebody. I had to be supportive when she was depressed, keeping her going. And when she had a thrombosis I felt guilty because I hadn't bullied her enough to get her doing exercises and walking again. Then there was organising things for her to do – bits of sewing, knitting. Taking up bits of food she could help prepare – so that she kept her self-respect, felt that she was still able to make a contribution. But I worried about how she was actually seeing herself.

Interviewer: How did you reassure yourself that you were doing enough?

Kate: I think that's an extremely difficult one. I looked at that list we made. It looks a lot when you write down what you actually do. It's quite reassuring to keep looking at your piece of paper and think, well, I'm really doing all this. You don't think of it as being much, but it is.

Interviewer: What were the pressures on you?

Kate: The biggest pressure was friends who would say, 'She's a bit shut away up there [Upstairs in the bedroom].' You put your own lines down and then other people push you to cross them. You feel so mean. You need a lot of strength. It's hard to say 'If I don't consider my own needs then the whole thing's going to fall apart anyway.' My husband used to answer, 'That's the whole point.' The other thing people would do was to say, 'How are you getting on looking after Granny? But still she's such a nice person.' And that was that – no possibility of saying it was hard after that. It's not personalities – it's the situation.

Interviewer: What helped you most?

Kate: There being two of us. I found it so helpful just to be able to moan – keeping the channels open between us so that we could talk it through. Sometimes he would say to his mother, 'Kate can't do this tomorrow', when I felt I couldn't say it. The other thing was having a break. We had a weekend to ourselves – three times she went to a good friend's not far away. I remember walking down the road with the toilet frame over my shoulder! But it was worth it. Anything you can laugh about is really a Godsend. (Extract from Rosie Bell and Sue Gibbons, *Working with Carers*, pages 54–5)

What information do you need if you are already caring?

Many more people who work in health or social services are now aware of the problems faced by people who care at home *as well as* the person being cared for. Unfortunately, there are still some who will assume that you are the healthy one and do not have any needs yourself. So, although any person coming into your home *should* ask after your own well-being in addition to the health of the person you look after, don't bank on it. Be prepared to offer information about help *you* would like to receive. This is the kind of information that is likely to be useful for anyone assessing your needs for help:

About caring

- What is your relationship to the person cared for (mother, son, wife . . .)?
- How old are you and the person you look after?
- Does anyone else live in the same house?
- Who is your GP? (Do you share the same GP?)
- What does the person you care for suffer from?
- Does the person you look after need help
  - to get in/out of bed
  - to get in/out of chair?
  - to walk?
  - to sit on lavatory/commode?
  - to clean afterwards?
  - to wash/shave/dress?
  - to eat?
  - other?
- Is the person incontinent? If so, do you have a washing machine?

About you

- Do you get enough sleep?
- Do you suffer from muscle strain or stiffness?
- Do you have other symptoms of exhaustion?
- Do you have any opportunity to have a break from caring?
- What is your most difficult problem?
- What would make life easier for you?
- Do you have any family nearby? Do they help?
- Do you have any other sources of help (e.g. social worker, care attendant, health visitor)?
- Do you receive attendance allowance?
- What do you miss most?
- Would you like to meet and talk with other carers?

Try working through this list: add or take away questions that may seem more relevant to you. There may not be immediate solutions to the things you find difficult now, but it is important to identify what the problem areas are before they get too overwhelming. Once you become overtired, it will be hard to see the wood for the trees and you might not be able to see that someone to help you at bed time would alleviate the strain, or perhaps the opportunity to walk in the park would give you the time you need to yourself.

Try to remain positive: just because you have managed unaided up to now does not mean you have to carry on in the same way. Although many services are suffering shortages of staff and money, many areas have realised the importance of providing help in the home and new services are being developed.

Do this exercise together with the person you look after if that feels right. In some cases, you may be both looking after each other – in which case you need to sort out between you what the mutual care involves.

If the whole family is involved it may help to sit down together to see if there are ways of sharing problems and identify how to bring extra help in. If you are alone, perhaps you could ask a trusted friend or someone from a local support group.

When you have answered the questions as well as you can, make a note of:

Things I find difficult are ....

....

I would like some help to ....

....

....

I need to find out about ....

....

....

Take these notes along with you when you go to visit any of the professionals who may help you. If you feel nervous about asking for help, take someone with you who can back you up. To give you both time to talk properly it is best to make an appointment. If it feels easier, you could write to the person before the appointment. This also gives him or her an opportunity to look out the information you need. If you feel you may forget important information, take notes of what the person says to you, or ask him or her to write it down.

You may have to arrange a number of appointments with different people and you might find it useful to be able to refer back to these meetings, particularly if you do not get what you want. Keep a record of:

- the date of the meeting
- who you talked to, name and job title
- what was said

8 Practical help

It is a fight to get anything but eventually I had visiting nurses, sitters, a day centre for my disabled husband, wheelchair repair and maintenance, bath aids and a real lifesaver – a carers' support group for myself.

At the time of writing, the future of both the National Health Service and community care are under discussion. The information in this chapter should still be accurate but may miss some detail. The main change of emphasis will be that the local authority social services department (or social work department for Scottish readers) will be responsible for co-ordinating services that will help you and the person you care for. They will have powers to use private and voluntary (or 'non-profit making') organisations to deliver these services, so you could find that the social services arrange for you to receive a service from a private agency who is working under contract to the social services department. The advantage to carers should be the fact that there is *one* place to go for help – the social services department.

The changes also recommend that you, the carer, should be consulted: particularly, for instance, when a relative is being discharged from hospital. In the jargon, a 'package of care' should be arranged for that person which may involve bringing in people to provide nursing, practical help and advice.

As with all change, it will be some time before the system runs to plan, so if you don't get what you need – keep trying.

Your rights

As a carer, or as a disabled person, you already have certain rights under the Disabled Persons (Services, Consultation and

Representation) Act 1986, which gives carers legal recognition
for the first time. This is potentially a very useful piece of
legislation for carers and disabled people. However, at the time
of writing, key sections of the Act have still not been
implemented and the government has recently indicated that it
does not see the Act as a good use of resources.

Under the Act, you can ask the social services department:

- to make an assessment (a written statement) on the needs of
  the person you are looking after
- to have your own ability to continue to provide care included
  in the assessment

The assessment of the disabled person's needs should take into
account the need for:

- help in the home
- recreational facilities both inside and outside the home
- assistance with transport to such facilities
- aids and adaptations
- holidays, meals, telephones

An assessment can make all the difference, as this carer
confirms:

If only I had known about the occupational therapist. We thought they
came round teaching you how to occupy your time weaving baskets.
We hadn't a clue about aids available through the social services. Now
we are well supplied with helpful gadgets to make life easier for all of
us and we also have a stair chair lift fitted with a grant from the
council.

The Act also says that the local authority must give you, and the
person you care for, information on services that are available.
That includes all the kinds of help that are described in this
chapter.

Where to start

So, your first step is the social services office (look in the
Yellow Pages phone book under Local Government). Ask if
they have a 'carers worker'. If not, ask to be put in touch with a
social worker at your local office. Also check to find out if there
is any further help by asking:

- other carers

- your doctor
- your hospital specialist
- your local advice centre or citizens advice bureau
- if applicable, your child's school or local education authority
- your local council for voluntary service or carers' support group (see chapter 9)
- your local library

Gathering the information

I would say to anyone caring: ask anyone and everyone for as much physical and mechanical help as you can get. The more assistance you get, the easier it is for you both.

You will probably end up gathering a lot of names and contacts, so it might be useful to buy an address book and start to collect useful addresses and telephone numbers. Or keep a piece of paper by your phone with the following:

Telephone numbers

- Doctor ....
- Hospital specialist ....
- Health visitor ....
- District nurse ....
- Social worker ....
- Occupational therapist ....
- Home help ....
- Dentist ....
- Optician ....
- Local voluntary organisation (Age Concern, MENCAP, etc) ....
- Carers' support group ....
- Care attendant/sitter ....
- Ambulance (in emergency, dial 999) ....
- Others ....

You will not be able to fill in all the spaces immediately, unless you have been caring for some time. Some may not be relevant to you and the person you look after, in which case turn to 'Who Does What?' (a glossary of job titles) on pages 122–5, and compile your own list.

Each time you come into contact with your doctor or another professional, ask him or her to supply you with names and numbers to complete your list. They may assume you already know about these people. You don't have to make contact immediately, but it can be reassuring to have the number handy of, say, your local support group, just in case you need it one day when things get too much.

There is a shortage of help in some areas but this is not always the reason you do not find out about help you could have. Sometimes carers such as Mrs Thomson struggle on for years, not knowing about simple things that could help them:

For years every Saturday morning I blanket bathed my husband as he couldn't manage the stairs to the bathroom. I reached cracking point and my doctor advised my husband to go into residential care while I had a holiday. He was overjoyed to have a bath. When he explained the reason to the staff, they sent an OT and we had no end of improvements: a shower unit, a raised toilet, sliding doors.

Who runs the services?

Care services may be run by the health authority or social services department or by private or voluntary organisations.

Private agencies can supply trained nurses and care assistants and there is a growing industry to meet all kinds of home care needs. You may be able to get this help through the social services if the agency has a contract to carry out work on their behalf.

If you can afford it, you may want to take up these options by paying for it yourself. Always try to get a recommendation from another carer and check you know all the costs involved.

Another way some people pay for private help is by a grant from the Independent Living Fund (see page 69). You should go to your social services department for advice; it is still their duty to co-ordinate home care provision.

Of course, it is not just a matter of finding out what is available. Sometimes you have to build up to a situation where, for example, you are able to take regular breaks. As Joan explains,

The Carers Worker came to visit us at home and handled the situation so well that Don agreed to have a 'sitter' so that I could have some time off to do some shopping. Later he agreed to day care one day a week which enabled me to have a complete day of freedom. Gradually my husband has become used to the centre and, having stayed there whilst I had a holiday, he has now agreed to stay there one week in each month. It's the only way to cope long term.

Joan's experience illustrates why it can be helpful to bring someone else in to help you: in this case the Carers Worker was able to persuade the husband to accept help which he would probably have refused if Joan had suggested it.

What services are there?

Below you will find listed the kind of help you would hope to expect in your area. This does not mean it will be readily available. It is often a matter of luck where you happen to be living.

Domestic help

Help with essential household chores can be provided by home helps who work for the social services department (or family aides, as they are sometimes called). In some areas, the traditional home help has been taken over by home carers who will undertake some domestic work but usually only in homes where the client needs personal care as well. Other people may be directed to private cleaning agencies.

Nursing help

Your doctor can ensure that you receive some home nursing help. The district nurse will call to carry out specific tasks like giving injections and changing dressings. An auxiliary nurse may help with bathing and washing. Sometimes there is a night nursing service to help put people to bed or to attend very ill people. This is probably not advertised as demand usually outstrips supply, but is worth finding out about in case you need it in the future.

Private nursing agencies are registered with the local authority company registration department. You should be able to get a list from your local authority, or you can look in the telephone directory or contact a branch of Age Concern.

Costs can be high and do not always reflect quality. Rates can vary from day to day as they are often calculated to take into account public holidays, additional travel for a change of nurse, etc. Always ask for a quotation that includes all extra expenses and compare the price with other agencies.

Short-term residential care

Your doctor or social worker can arrange for 'respite care' to allow you to take a break. They can arrange admission to a local hospital, a social services residential home, a special hostel or

unit or a private nursing home. Some areas have 'link' or 'foster'
families who will take the person you look after. Hospices may
also be able to offer short stays for people suffering from cancer
and some other serious illnesses (see below). In many parts of
the country, respite care is in short supply, so you may need to
be quite persistent to find the care that suits you and the person
you look after.

Day hospitals or centres

Day hospitals aim to provide rehabilitation and treatment:
referral is usually through the doctor or community nursing
service. It may only be available for a limited time. Day centres
have a more social function and you can find out about these
from your local social services department. Some day centres
may be run by voluntary organisations, often under contract to
social services.

Hospice care

Almost all hospices are for people who have cancer or a similar
life-threatening illness. Some specialise in caring for people with
AIDS. People generally stay for weeks rather than months, and
sometimes hospice care can be given in your home by
MacMillan nurses (specially trained nurses who are funded by
the MacMillan fund).

In general, there is no charge although a small number will
ask for a contribution towards patient care. Most hospices are
independent – many are registered charities but work closely
with the health services. MacMillan Continuing Care units are
now funded and run by the NHS. Two national charitable
organisations also run homes: the Marie Curie Memorial
Foundation and the Sue Ryder Foundation.

Hospice care is usually carried out by multi-disciplinary teams
who provide expertise and advice in pain relief and symptom
control and who give emotional support to patients and carers.
Referral is always by a doctor, but there is nothing to stop you
contacting a hospice first if you want to know more about how
it runs.

Children's hospices will admit children who have life-
threatening diseases for short-term respite care – even if the
illness has not reached the terminal stage.

For any general queries about hospices, contact the Hospice
Information Service (see page 140).

Loan of equipment

You can borrow commodes, bathing aids and so on from the
social services department or through a voluntary organisation
like the Red Cross. It is worth asking for a visit from the
occupational therapist (commonly abbreviated to OT and
working for the social services department or the hospital)
because s/he will assess your needs and may be able to offer
further advice. Play equipment, jigsaws and puzzles may also be
loaned from a toy library – ask the OT.

You can also buy equipment from commercial suppliers.
Always ask for a demonstration first – preferably in your home.
A second best is to visit a showroom where the appliances can
be demonstrated.

Sitting services

A sitter will stay with the person you look after in your home
to allow you to have time off or to do other chores. Care
attendants may also help you at difficult times of the day:
getting someone out of bed in the morning or back to bed late
at night. These are very often organised by voluntary
organisations, but the local social services department should
have information about them. Services vary from quite informal
schemes with volunteers to professionally trained and paid
workers. The Crossroads Care Attendant Schemes are highly
recommended by many carers for their flexible and
individually-tailored service: a care attendant is generally
recruited to take over from the carer for agreed periods of time.
To find out if there is one near you, contact the headquarters,
listed on page 129. In some areas, the statutory services (health
and social services) will provide sitters themselves. Private
agencies also offer a home care service. If you are dealing with
them directly, check you are aware of all the costs involved
before committing yourself. The United Kingdom Home Care
Association (UKHCA) aims to promote high standards in the
private sector and should be able to advise you (see page 141).

Housing adaptations

You may need to widen doors or build ramps in your home to
accommodate a wheelchair or you may even need to build an
extra room. If you live in a council house, adaptations are
usually paid for by the local authority. If not, you may be able
to get financial help from other sources: ask your social worker
or occupational therapist for advice. Your local authority

housing department should also give advice. Do not carry out any work before you have had your claim agreed in writing.

Transport

Some local authorities operate schemes to assist people with disabilities to travel on reduced fares on local buses. (For further information about financial help see chapter 10). They may also be able to give you information about community transport schemes for help travelling to and from hospital. Also contact your local transport authority, the council for voluntary service, or the rural community council if you live in the country.

Education

If you are caring for a child with special needs over the age of 2, the local education authority must make an assessment of your child's needs if you ask for it. The key people who should be able to give you advice about services for your child are the social worker, health visitor or the special needs adviser who works for your local education authority.

Special carers' projects

In a few parts of the country, there are carers' centres or special support projects which are designed to help carers. Your doctor or social services office should know if there is one in your area. The joy of these schemes is that they can save you the bother of searching out what help is around. These projects will often deal with all kinds of requests quite unrelated to caring. A crisis is a crisis when you are caring at home – whether it is blocked plumbing or a swarm of bees in the sitting room!

For details of support groups, see chapter 9.

Employing your own help

Some carers have established successful arrangements by advertising for paid help through the local paper. If you do this, you must be prepared to act as an employer, paying the going rate for the job, and taking responsibility for PAYE and national insurance. You will need to word your advertisement carefully and interview applicants in the presence of the person you look after. Make sure the conditions of employment are clear on both sides: flexibility and number of hours, what the work involves and so on. Suggest a trial period to see how it works out on both sides.

You can get further advice from your local jobcentre who can supply you with leaflets from the Department of Employment on the responsibilities of employers and employees' rights. For advice on national insurance, go to the local Department of Social Security and speak to your local tax office. You may also want to contact a solicitor if you need to draw up a contract of employment.

Help in a crisis

Caring at home is often a series of minor and major crises, which tend to always happen in the middle of the night or a bank holiday! The emergency services will respond to a call at any time. It may not be a matter of life and death, but sometimes you may find yourself in a fix:

I had him stuck in the bath. I tried not to panic – just released the plug, dried him off in the bath and dried the bath itself. I dressed him in his top clothes and made a cup of tea and a comfortable bed in the bath until I could get help. My neighbour came to my rescue, otherwise I would have called the Ambulance Service.

9 Other sources of help

Friends disappear like rabbits down holes – and when girlfriends hear of auntie they're away into the hills.

Involving other people in home caring can bring benefits for yourself and the person you are caring for. New faces and a varied routine will reduce the dependency that can otherwise develop between the two of you. Other people, too, will feel more involved as they recognise the value of their contributions.

Shared caring

Some carers do not have any immediate family to turn to. For those who do have relatives, sharing responsibility for care is rarely straightforward. A combination of unspoken expectations and practical difficulties – particularly if some members of the family live far away – can often mean that one person carries most of the load. This can happen when people make assumptions about who should do the caring: often the nearest female relative who may already have other responsibilities.

A woman can feel it is her duty to respond to this subtle pressure and will often volunteer to take on the care of a relative even when she is in poor health herself or has financial worries. 'Duty' is a powerful motivator because to fail in your duty is to fail in the eyes of the people close to you as Jill Pitkeathley, director of the Carers National Association describes in her book *It's My Duty Isn't It?* (1989).

Many carers say that asking family for help is more difficult than asking for services. As Grace explained, 'It's like asking for love: it should be freely given.' But if it is not freely given, it is not always because others are unwilling. It may be that they do not realise how tiring the work is, or they do not know how to help. Are you contributing to this impression, or do you talk together about how things really are? Connie describes how the behaviour of her husband made it hard for her to explain her distress:

I found that when close members of the family came to visit, my husband was always on his best behaviour . . . he had developed a lot of frustration from not being able to talk and had started being violent towards me. It's almost as if they don't believe you and it's an awful feeling.

Talking together is important if you can: tell your relatives what happens when they are not there and ask for regular help. It can be a small favour – such as taking the person you care for out for a drive or a walk once a fortnight – but it is a good idea to try to introduce an activity that maintains some regular contact, especially if you are caring alone.

Friends, neighbours and volunteers

Again, friends and neighbours vary in their ability to cope with illness and disability. Sometimes people are not aware of the extra strains of caring.

Parents who are looking after a child with special needs may find others make the assumption that because their child is young, he or she is somehow easier to manage. In reality the condition of the child may mean regular and onerous trips to hospitals accompanied by other able-bodied children in the family.

Caring for a child with special needs is not simply an extension of parenting: it involves complex negotiations with the health, education and social services on top of the ordinary demands of a young family. This may be obvious to you as a parent carer, but you may need to talk about it to friends and family.

Friends will rally round in a crisis, but with a chronic condition it is easy to lose touch with people over time as your own energy and time for socialising is restricted. Some close friends will be frightened by the illness, or they may be in awe of what you are doing if they feel they could not take on a similar responsibility. Joan regretted the falling off of visits from her husband's friends after his stroke, but grew to accept their fear: 'The men started to back away. They'd look at George and think it might be them.'

Instead, she found an ally in a neighbour who she had hardly known before George's illness who came round to visit regularly with his dog. The dog, Joan claimed, was the best therapy for George! In fact, pets and babies crop up regularly in carers' examples of what helps to cheer them up. If you are virtually housebound, you can start to feel apart from the ordinary flow of life. Doris finds letters a great help, '. . . especially newsy letters. I enter someone else's more sane life for a while and I find it a relief to "talk" to them as I write a reply'.

If someone offers to help, try to give them a practical task to do. They are more likely to feel they have achieved something and may offer again. It may be easier to arrange for someone to come in to read to the person you care for than 'just to keep Beth company for an hour'. Try making a list of jobs that could be done by others, for example:

- Take for a drive or to the park
- Help with daily exercises
- Wash and cut hair
- Play games together
- Bring in tapes of talks, sermons or meetings unable to attend
- Help look after plants, window boxes
- Bring animal or child to visit
- Go to tea together
- Bring along music – tapes or records

Some tasks may not involve the person you look after, but can ease the general load for you. It may be up to you to spell out to people how they can help, but they will often be very willing. Perhaps you can ask someone to help with:

- Occasional shopping
- Odd jobs around the house
- Trips to the library (some places operate a housebound service)
- Making a meal once in a while
- Calling in for a chat

How can voluntary organisations help?

If you do not know anybody in your immediate circle who can help out in this way, you may be able to find help through local voluntary organisations. The traditional role of voluntary organisations has been to run 'fringe' activities to supplement state provision, but this government is increasing the use of voluntary organisations to provide services such as day centres.

To find out what is happening in your area, contact the volunteer bureau or council for voluntary service if there is one, or approach organisations that usually have a number of willing volunteers, such as the Women's Royal Voluntary Service (WRVS), Red Cross and Age Concern.

You will still find a number of the more traditional small organisations organised by local people, a core of volunteers and maybe one or two paid staff.

In most areas there are local organisations and charities representing particular illnesses and conditions. By contacting one of these, you will meet others who understand what you are living through and can pass on information and advice from their own experience. It will not be all one way: you will probably find that you have useful tips to pass on and the support will be mutual.

Sometimes it helps to have the backing of a voluntary organisation when you are trying to get services you know you are entitled to. Often local organisations will back you up in your struggle to get proper respite care or help in the home. The organisation may be already campaigning to get these services.

Voluntary organisations run all kinds of useful and imaginative schemes, but these are some examples of the help you may be able to find:

- transport
- financial advice or assistance
- counselling or informal emotional support through home visits or mutual support groups
- loan of aids and equipment: hoists, commodes, etc (especially Red Cross) and loan of toys and games
- advice about 'gadgets' to help in day-to-day living: tin openers for weak wrists, cups that don't spill, etc. (often Age Concern)
- schemes to help you get a break, e.g. holiday play schemes or sitting services for adults
- advice about how to cope with hospitals, social services, etc.
- information specific to the illness or condition of the person you look after
- home visiting educational help for slow developing children, e.g. Portage projects (see National Portage Association on page 132)
- befriending – where a volunteer links up with someone with

special needs to share activities and to develop friendship
- citizen advocacy – where a volunteer speaks on behalf of another person to help that person defend or exercise their rights

If you are a carer, there are two key organisations to look out for in your local area:

- The Carers National Association has already been mentioned. Find out if there is a local branch (see page 130 for the headquarters' address).
- The Crossroads Care Attendant Scheme is often a lifeline to carers. Check to see if there is one locally. Crossroads can provide trained care attendants to come into your home, offering a few hours' relief on a regular basis to suit you. If you cannot find a local contact, try writing to the headquarters' address on page 129.

What can a carers' support group offer?

It was such a relief to hear other people say the things I'd been feeling but felt so guilty about. I also learnt we could claim attendance allowance which as made all the difference.

Most groups describe their purpose as being to provide friendly support and information sharing. Some groups invite speakers and arrange outings and social functions; other groups concentrate more on creating a safe, intimate atmosphere where members can express their feelings about caring in the home. Many groups have established links with the local statutory and voluntary services, and most of the well attended groups are able to provide occasional sitters and advice about practical support.

Some groups are run by social services staff, community nurses or people working on behalf of voluntary organisations (such as Age Concern, Alzheimer's Disease Society, MIND, Carers National Association), and some groups are set up by private individuals who are, or have been, caring themselves.

A carers' support group may run fortnightly or monthly, usually for an hour or two. The majority of the people attending will be caring for a relative or partner in the home, some members may be recently bereaved, other members may be 'professionals' (social workers, nurses, home helps) who are able to provide advice and information. Most groups are open to any carer wishing to attend, some specialise in specific

OTHER SOURCES OF HELP 61

conditions – for example carers of people who have suffered strokes.

Parent carers may prefer to join a parents' group, particularly where their child is needing constant medical treatment. Other parents can be a mine of information and reassurance, about local paediatricians, education services and local help. At first it may be hard to speak up in a meeting, but no one will mind. One carer describes how she made a friend who helped her realise she was not alone with her worries:

At one meeting, I heard someone stand up and voice a worry high on my list. As the meeting closed I rushed to catch her up before she left the building. We discovered our sons knew each other and I know I have someone to share problems with now.

Conversations at carers' groups are not all doom and gloom: it is often an opportunity to get helpful advice and to have a good laugh. Humour is not at the expense of the person being looked after, but comes from the unexpected situations carers find themselves in.

The practical difficulties of attending meetings mean most groups tolerate erratic attendance, and it is often quite acceptable not to attend meetings at all, but to be on the mailing list for information.

A support group is not a panacea for all problems. Not everyone wants to attend a group. For some people, though, a group can provide an emotional outlet, it can offer social contact with people who understand and it can provide time for the *carer* apart from the person s/he cares for.

How to contact a group

All the suggestions given below for contacting local voluntary organisations apply. The Carers National Association can tell you if there is a local group or, if you are caring for someone under 19, Contact a Family can help (see page 130 for addresses). They can also give you advice if you want to set up a group yourself. You will also find a list of further reading on page 128 to guide you in setting up your own self-help group.

How to find out about local organisations

- There will probably be an umbrella group which is in contact with most of the voluntary organisations in your area. It may be called: council for voluntary service/community action/ volunteer bureau/rural community council.

- Ask your citizens advice bureau.
- Your library or town hall should have a list. Don't take this as the last word on what is available as new groups spring up all the time which may not be listed.
- Ask any of the services you are in contact with: the hospital, your social workers or district nurse or keep an eye out for notices in the doctor's surgery.
- There may be a DIAL–Disablement and Advice line in your area which can tell about local services available to people with disabilities and their carers.
- Contact a national organisation and ask if they have any local contacts (some are listed on pages 129–41, others you will find in *The Voluntary Agencies Directory* published by Bedford Square Press in your library).
- Ask friends, relatives or other carers.

How can a national voluntary organisation help?

Apart from directing you to local contacts, national organisations sometimes have specialist services. Most can offer advice on a range of topics relating to caring at home and will be able to give you more detailed information on specific conditions, ailments and disabilities. Here are a few examples of special services offered by national bodies.

Mutual support

Parents looking after a child suffering from a rare condition can be put in touch with families in other parts of the country whose child suffers the same condition by writing to, or phoning, Contact a Family (see page 130). They will also deal with any query or problem you might have looking after a child with special needs.

Backing to help you fight for allowances

People sometimes have problems getting the financial help they need because of a lack of official understanding about the special needs of the person they care for. For example, people suffering from Cystic Fibrosis have special dietary needs because they are not able to absorb the nutrients in a normal diet: the Cystic Fibrosis Research Trust (see page 131) will write a letter of support for carers who are seeking extra allowances to cover food.

Finance

Some national charities are able to assist individuals financially, such as the Cancer Relief Macmillan Fund, which can help with holiday costs for people with cancer and their families. To apply, you need to ask your social worker or family doctor. Further advice is available from Cancerlink (see page 130).

Specialist advice

After being given a diagnosis of a rare and incurable illness many families feel devastated and at a loss. For example, a diagnosis of Motor Neurone Disease may take a long time while other possibilities are eliminated. As yet, the cause of MND is unknown and there is no know cure. The GP may never have encountered a case before and, because the incidence of MND is low, there is unlikely to be someone else nearby who can give advice. The MND Association (see page 131) can give constructive help in ways of managing the condition and of helping to maintain the independence and well-being of the sufferer.

Lobbying for change

If you are not happy with the quality of help in your area and have not been successful in getting support locally, let a national organisation know. Many have contact with national government departments and can influence policy. Where it is a case of changing the law, national organisations will lobby Parliament and successful cases have been fought based on the injustices suffered by individuals.

Community support

Adult education often offer classes that are very helpful to carers. Many centres run classes in relaxation, stress management and assertiveness training – all skills that carers need to use daily. Some may even run classes in home nursing skills: how to lift a patient, managing incontinence and so on. But perhaps you want to get away from caring altogether and want to take advantage of other opportunities that arise to explore languages, art or other interests you may have.

Many centres are keen to broaden their access to more people in the community, so if leaving your relative or partner is a problem, try talking to the administrator about it. Some more enlightened places have made arrangements with social services or with local Crossroads schemes to enable people to attend classes. There may be classes that would be suitable for the person you look after: centres should cater for disabled people in their mainstream classes and some may have classes suitable for people with learning difficulties.

Depending on your local area, there may be a number of other places you could make more social contacts and possibly find help:

- For women carers, there may be a women's centre where they can call or drop in for a chat.
- Black or ethnic minority carers may feel more comfortable talking to someone who shares their cultural background even if they do not have the experience of being a carer. Try contacting your nearest community relations council or one of the regional offices of the Commission for Racial Equality (see page 130).
- The local church, temple or religious group may offer to visit in the home or lend support and encouragement.
- A local college or university will probably have a 'community action' group who may run holiday playschemes for children or volunteer visiting schemes in the local community.
- Other groups such as women's institutes and rotary clubs organise fundraising and social events and may be able to help in practical ways.
- For people who have been, or are, in employment and in a trade union, the welfare officer may be able to give guidance or financial assistance or informal help.

10 Money matters

After 12 years of caring, my advice to anyone about to start is to make sure you are getting all the allowances available. Pride and independence are all very well but they don't pay the bills!

Caring at home is a costly business. You may have to meet extra housing, medical and transport costs. This can be at a time when your income is reduced: many people have to leave work to be a carer, some have to retire early with loss of a full pension. Younger carers may have to forfeit promotion or reduce their hours in order to care for someone at home, or perhaps the person you are looking after has been the main wage earner.

There are other hidden costs: if it is difficult to leave the house for long, you may find you have to shop in local, more expensive shops. You may have heavy laundry and cleaning bills and you may be paying more for special food, heating or clothing.

There are a number of allowances or 'benefits' you can claim. Even *with* these allowances people with disabilities and their carers are generally worse off because of home caring.

The information below is correct at the time of writing, but do find someone to advise you as there may be other allowances you, or the person you look after, can claim that are not listed here.

For further advice contact:

- Your local department of social security (DSS) for information, leaflets and applications forms, or you can ring the free telephone line on 0800-666555 (9.00–4.30).
- Welfare rights advisers who will give you impartial advice

and may help you to work out your budget. Look out for
welfare rights units or law centres, citizens advice bureaux,
carers' projects, local Age Concern groups, etc.
● Contact the local carers' group, or speak to others in a similar
  position to yourself.
● See the *Disability Rights Handbook* available from your library
  or from the Disability Alliance Educational and Research
  Association (see page 131).

Are you claiming these allowances?

There are several allowances which do not depend on your
financial situation which you should look into immediately if
you do not already receive them.

Attendance allowance

This is an allowance paid direct to the person who is ill or
disabled. It is tax-free and is not means tested. There is a higher
rate paid when the person needs attendance night and day. As
from April 1990, this allowance is now extended to children
with special needs under 2 years old. There is no upper age
limit. Normally you have to show that the person has needed
the attendance for six months, but this rule is waived if the
person has a terminal illness.

Attendance allowance is paid if a person needs frequent
attention with 'bodily functions' (washing, dressing, eating,
toileting, getting in or out of bed) or needs supervision 'to
prevent a danger to themselves or others'.

It is worth applying for attendance allowance, even though
you have to go through the bother of a medical, because it is a
ticket to other help:

● invalid care allowance for the carer
● road tax exemption for some people barred from mobility
  allowance
● payments from the Independent Living Fund
● extra premiums with income support and/or housing benefit
  and poll tax benefit

The Disability Alliance Educational Research Association has
produced a guide for claimants who are turned down and wish
to reapply, called *Attendance Allowance: Going for a Review*
available from the address listed on page 131.

Invalid care allowance (ICA)

This is the only 'carer's benefit' that is paid directly to you in recognition of your caring work at home. You are entitled to claim it if you spend at least 35 hours a week looking after someone who receives attendance allowance (see below). You do not have to be living under the same roof, nor do you have to be related to the person you care for. ICA is not means tested, but it is taxable. If you earn over £20 a week (1990 figure) you cannot get ICA, nor can you claim ICA for the first time after reaching pensionable age.

If you are already getting other allowances, or someone is claiming on your behalf, you may not get the full benefit of ICA, but it is still worth claiming as it helps to protect your pension record.

Mobility allowance

This is a tax-free allowance for people who are unable or virtually unable to walk due to a physical disability, or whose health is put at risk by the effort of walking. It is possible for some autistic or mentally handicapped people to qualify for mobility allowance. People who are both deaf and blind can also claim.

You must claim before you are 66, but if you are eligible you will go on receiving it until 80. It is not means tested. If you receive mobility allowance you can get special travel concessions on British Rail, an automatic 'orange badge' for parking and exemption from road tax.

The Disability Alliance has produced a guide on how to present your case and how to appeal if you are turned down, available from the address listed on page 131.

The government has recently announced proposals for changing disability benefits. You should contact your local citizens advice bureau for current information. The major change could be the introduction of a specific 'disability benefit' for the under 65s which would replace attendance and mobility allowances.

Poll tax/community charge exemption

People who suffer from dementia or mental impairment should not have to pay the community charge. You will need a certificate from your doctor: the term that is used is 'severely mentally impaired'. At the time of writing this exemption does not extend to other groups of people who are impaired by profound physical handicaps, but national voluntary organisations are campaigning to change this.

Another way to reduce your poll tax bill, at least for the first three years, is to claim 'transitional relief'. This is available to all people with disabilities or pensioners who were not paying rates – in other words, living with relatives. It is not means tested but it has to be *claimed* from the council – it is not an automatic exemption.

If you are on a low income, you may be able to claim a rebate. Anyone on income support or equivalent income will get an 80 per cent rebate. As income rises, so the rebate falls. You cannot claim if you have savings over £16,000.

It is your right to apply for these allowances. The sums may not be huge, but they can make a great difference to your quality of life. As Mrs Mackie said, 'If only I had known before that I could have had financial help like ICA and attendance allowance. We just assumed if one of us couldn't work the other would have to.'

Are you on a low income?

If so, there will be a number of allowances you or the person you care for can claim. You need to get individual advice about this as the following information is not comprehensive.

Income support

This is available if you or your partner are not in full-time paid work (over 24 hours a week) and have savings of less than £8,000. Income support includes extra payments, called 'premiums' for carers, disabled people and pensioners. Income support is often useful to 'top up' other income such as retirement pension or sickness benefits.

Once you are receiving income support, you can get: full housing and health benefits, and you may be able to claim loans or 'community care grants' from the Social Fund to pay for single items or to help in a sudden crisis.

Family credit

If you have children and are working over 24 hours a week and have savings of less than £8,000 you may claim this benefit. The amount you get depends on your income and the number of children you have. Calculations are complex so find an expert to help you work it out.

Housing benefit

Regardless of your hours of work, you can claim for help with paying rent and community charge if you are on a low income. If you claim income support you automatically qualify for maximum housing benefit. If you do not claim income support, apply to your local council.

Making changes

In spite of the benefits that are available, many carers still find that their standard of living drops considerably as a direct result of taking on caring responsibilities. A national campaign called 'Caring Costs' is trying to achieve an adequate income for all carers. It is calling for:

- a flat rate allowance to be paid to all carers who provide a substantial amount of care
- invalid care allowance to be paid at the same rate as 'income' benefits such as retirement pension
- further relaxation of the ICA earnings limit
- widening of the entitlement to income support premium

If you feel carers are entitled to a better deal, speak to your local MP and send for further information to 'Caring Costs' at the Carers National Association.

Other help available to carers

My advice to everyone is don't sit back and passively accept impossible situations. Ask, shout, until you find what you need for both of you to have a better quality of life. We now have an electric bed hoist, ramps and an electric chair.

Independent Living Fund

This is a discretionary trust fund which can give financial help to enable very severely disabled people to live at home. Money can be granted for a personal carer, domestic help or for special items of equipment which can increase independence. The system is complex but generally is open to people who are claiming attendance allowance and who are on a low income.

Apply for form ILF 100 from: The Independent Living Fund, PO Box 183, Nottingham NG8 3RD.

Family Fund

The Family Fund is financed by the government and run by the

Joseph Rowntree Memorial Trust. It is for families who have children with severe disabilities up to the age of 16. There is no strict means test, but your financial situation will be taken into account, and you should be able to show that you have approached all the usual sources for help (listed above) before applying. In the past grants have been given for: laundry equipment, car hire, driving lessons for carers isolated by their caring, clothing or holidays. But you can apply for any exceptional expense.

Obtain an applicaiton form from: The Family Fund, PO Box 50, York YO1 1UY.

Family Welfare Association

This organisation administers a range of different trust funds. Applications need to be made by a social worker on your behalf. For further information contact: The Grants Officer, 501-505 Kingsland Road, London E8 4AU, tel. 071-254 6251.

Charitable grants

The Directory of Social Change produces a practical guide to sources of money available from trusts and charities, called *A Guide to Grants for Individuals in Need*. You should find a copy at your local reference library or citizens advice bureau.

Getting out and about

The worst thing was the isolation. I didn't see another soul from one day to the next. Then I found out we wouldn't have to pay tax on the car, so we bought an old banger and with the Orange Badge Scheme we can park in the centre of town and see friends.

The mobility allowance has already been mentioned, but there are a number of other sources of financial help to assist you on private and public transport.

Road tax exemption

If a car is regularly used to transport a disabled person who receives mobility allowance or attendance allowance, the car may be exempt from road tax.

Motability scheme

This is a government-backed voluntary scheme set up to help people to use the mobility allowance to buy or rent a car or

wheelchair. For more information apply to: Motability, 2nd
Floor, Gate House, Westward, Essex CM20 1HR, tel. 0279-
635666.

Orange Badge scheme

This gives free parking and longer time limits on street parking
for a car driver or a passenger who is disabled or blind. To
apply, contact your social services office.

Disabled person's railcard

British Rail offers concessionary fares and will make special
arrangements for access, toilets, seat reservations, etc. Discounts
also extend to the carer or companion on the journey.

Getting to and from hospital

If you are regularly visiting someone in hospital, you may be
able to claim help with your fares if you are on a low income.
Ask at the hospital or at your local DSS office. In some areas
there are voluntary driver schemes which may make a small
charge for petrol. Your local council for voluntary service or
citizens advice bureau should know of local schemes.

Useful publications

- *Door to Door* is a free comprehensive guide to transport for
  disabled people. Write (no stamp needed) to: *Door to Door*
  Guide, Freepost, Victoria Road, South Ruislip, Middlesex
  HA4 ONZ.
- The 'Care in the Air' leaflet gives advice for disabled air
  travellers. Write to: The Secretary, Air Transport Users
  Committee, 129 Kingsway, London SC2B 6NN, tel. 071-242
  3882.
- RADAR and Age Concern (see pages 132 and 129) both have
  a number of useful factsheets on transport.

Planning ahead

We had always shared decisions about money but there were times
when he just wasn't 'there' any more and I realised I would have to
shoulder the responsibility for the house and the kids on my own. It
was a lonely time, but once I got some legal advice I felt much better.

When the future is uncertain, thinking about money can be
difficult because it may mean you have to allow yourself to

think about the decline or death of someone you hold dear. This may go against the grain if you are fighting to remain optimistic. If you are a parent you may have to think about how your child will manage after you are gone.

It may just be that your elderly relative is gradually becoming forgetful. Whatever your situation, it is best to plan for these things, and to discuss them with the person concerned, than to cope with them in the throes of a crisis. Many of the national voluntary organisations listed on pages 129–39 have professional legal advisers who will be able to give you free advice.

Annuities

The most pressing concern for many parent carers is how to provide for their child's future after they die. Shortage of appropriate residential care in the community makes this a very real problem. The national voluntary organisations, such as MENCAP, can give help and advice. Some insurance companies will consider annuities for the future financial security of dependent relatives.

Collecting pensions and benefits

You can become the 'appointee' by filling in form BF56 at your local DSS office which allows you to collect pensions or benefits on behalf of the person you look after.

Power of attorney

The person you look after can give you the legal right to make financial decisions on his or her behalf. It is best to get the help and advice of a local solicitor. Your local law centre can advise about how to get legal aid if necessary. 'Enduring power of attorney' carries through if the person becomes mentally confused, but it must be organised *before* this arises with the consent of that person.

Court of Protection

This is intended to protect the affairs of people who are mentally infirm. The Court can appoint another person as a 'receiver' to take over the financial affairs under the Court's supervision. Administration fees are charged, as well as a registration fee. A law centre or citizens advice bureau should be able to help you. It is important to get legal advice as a

solicitor will be able to look more dispassionately at the future
and the need to plan for all eventualities.

A living will

This concerns treatment, not money, but may be of interest to
some readers. A living will is a form of 'anticipated' consent
when someone who is rational and able to make decisions
makes a written declaration about what should happen if they
become seriously ill and for some reason can no longer consent
to or refuse treatment. At present this has no legal status in
Britain, but it may help relieve worries about the future: some
doctors like to know the advance wishes of a patient because it
may help in making decisions about treatment. For further
information see a working party report called *The Living Will*
published by Edward Arnold (1988).

11 Making a complaint

I only got help because I was determined to get hold of it. I can imagine someone who wasn't persevering and didn't mind kicking up a fuss could have a hard time.

If you are not happy about the standard of services (or lack of services) you are receiving, the first step is always to discuss the matter with the worker or organisation concerned and try to resolve the problem informally. Sometimes the problem may not be one that can be solved in this way and you will have to pursue the matter formally.

A local law centre will be able to advise you and put you in touch with a solicitor if necessary, or you might be able to link up with someone who knows their way around the system and can take up your case on your behalf.

Social services

Under the terms of new community care legislation, it is the duty of local authority social service departments to assess the need for help in the home and to co-ordinate care services. They are also responsible for monitoring standards of care, including any private or voluntary services that are contracted to carry out the work. Local authorities must produce plans for the development of community care services which are open to inspection. At the time of writing it is unclear whether any formal appeal and complaint procedures will be in place. Whether or not this is the case, there are still formal steps you can take.

1 Discuss your dissatisfaction with the worker concerned. The

senior officer should write to acknowledge the complaint and try to resolve it.

2 If you want to take it further, ask for an official complaints form which will be sent to the divisional director who should reply in writing explaining what action will be taken.

3 If you are still dissatisfied, submit your complaint to the director of social services.

4 If the response is not adequate, complain to a member of the authority – i.e. a local councillor. Many councillors hold local surgeries for people to come and discuss problems. Your local town hall or reference library can give you more information and the name of your local councillor.

5 As a last resort, you can refer your local authority to the Secretary of State for Social Services, who has powers to override local authority decisions. By this stage you will probably want the backing of a voluntary organisation or a solicitor. For cases of maladministration or delay in service provision, contact the local Ombudsman either via a local councillor or directly to the address that covers your area;

For Scotland:
5 Shandwick Place
Edinburgh EH2 4RG
Tel. 031-229 4472

For Wales:
Derwent House
Court Road
Bridgend
Mid-Glamorgan
Wales CF31 1BN
Tel. 0656-61325

For the North of England and North Midlands:
29 Castlegate
York YO1 1RN
Tel. 0904-30151

For Greater London, the South East, East Anglia, the South and West of England and the West and East Midlands:
21 Queen Anne's Gate
London SW1H 9BU
Tel. 071-222 5622

For Northern Ireland:
33 Wellington Place
Belfast BT1 6HN
Tel. 0232-33821

Social security benefits

If you disagree with a decision about a Department of Social Security (DSS) benefit, you usually have a right of appeal. You will probably find it helpful to contact your local citizens advice bureau or a local advice or law centre to check on your rights. Sometimes they will even represent you if there is a tribunal. Notify the local DSS office of your decision to appeal in writing, within three months of the decision.

For other complaints, for instance about the way that decisions are made, write to the manager of the DSS office. If you are still not satisfied, write to your MP and ask him or her to make a complaint to the Parliamentary Ombudsman.

Health services

Your local community health council is a consumer 'watchdog' and can advise you about who and how to complain. In Scotland, it is called the Health Council.

1 Talk to the worker(s) concerned and try to resolve the matter informally.
2 Put your complaint in writing to the general manager of the health authority. The Community Health Council will tell you who is responsible. Keep a copy of your letter and keep all replies you receive.
3 If you are still not satisfied, you can put your complaint in writing to the Health Service Commissioner (also known as the Health Service Ombudsman).

Health Service Commissioner for England
Church House
Great Smith Street
London SW1P 3BW
Tel. 071-276 2035

Health Service Commissioner for Wales
4th Floor
Pearl Assurance House
Greyfriars Road
Cardiff CF1 3AG
Tel. 0222-394621

Health Service Commissioner for Scotland
2nd Floor
11 Melville Crescent
Edinburgh EH3 7LU
Tel. 031-225 7465

Commission for Complaints, Northern Ireland
Progressive House
33 Wellington Place
Belfast BT2 6HN
Tel 0232-233 821

Doctors

If you are not satisfied with the care and clinical judgement of
your family doctor:

1 Discuss your complaint with the doctor and try to resolve it
   informally.
2 For readers in England and Wales, put your complaint in
   writing to the Family Practitioner Committee which will be
   listed in the phone book (or you can find it through your
   Community Health Council). The name of this agency is
   being changed and may be listed as the 'Family Health
   Services Authority'. They also have 'lay conciliators' who will
   meet with you in your home and try to resolve the matter
   informally.

   Scottish readers should address complaints to the Health
   Board. People living in Northern Ireland should write to the
   Director of Public Health of the Health Board where the
   doctor is registered (this will be on your medical card). If you
   are unsure where or who to write to, contact the Chief
   Administrative Officer at the Central Services Agency, 25
   Adelaide Street, Belfast BT2 8FH, tel. 0232-324 431.

Complaints about unethical behaviour of a doctor should be
sent to the General Medical Council, 44 Hallam Street, London
W1N 5LF, tel. 071-580 7642.

Special education

If you are not satisfied with the plans put forward for the
special educational needs of your child by your local education
authority (LEA):

1 Speak to the named officer who is concerned with the
   assessment.
2 If you are still not satisfied, you can go to the local Appeal
   Committee. The Committee cannot overrule the LEA, but can
   comment on its plans and ask the LEA to reconsider them.
3 If you are not happy with the way in which the LEA reviews
   its decision, or if the Appeal Committee supports the original

plan, you can appeal to the Secretary of State for Education who has the power to confirm the statement, make changes to it or tell the LEA to abandon it. You can also appeal to the Secretary of State if the LEA has decided not to assess your child and you feel that an assessment *should* be made.

Mental health services

The Mental Health Act Commission is a special health authority which monitors detained patients (those on 'sections'). Commissioners regularly visit hospitals. Complaints concerning informal patients should go to the administrator of the hospital or day centre concerned.

1 As always, try to clear the matter informally by talking to the people concerned.
2 Put your complaint in writing to the hospital manager. Ask your local community health council who is the person responsible.
3 If you are not happy with the response, put your complaint in writing to the Mental Health Act Commission at the address nearest you:

Liverpool
Cressington House
249 St Mary's Road
Garston
Liverpool L19 0NF
Tel. 051-427 2061

London
Hepburn House
Marsham Street
London SW1P 4HW
Tel. 071-6016/6008

Northern Ireland
Elizabeth House
116–118 Holywood Road
Belfast BT4 1NY
Tel. 0232-651157

Nottingham
Spur A
Block 5
Government Buildings
Chalfont Drive

Western Boulevard
Nottingham NG8 3RZ
Tel. 0602-410304

Scotland
25 Drumfheugh Gardens
Edinburgh EH3 7RB
Tel. 031-225 7034

MIND (see page 131) can give free legal advice on these
matters as well as details of solicitors who may help.

National policy

Many of the problems carers encounter cannot be solved locally
but need changes in national policy. If you would like more
people to know about the problems:

- speak to your MP
- write to the local (or national) newspapers – or try to get a
  journalist interested in the issue. Ask local radio or TV to
  look into the subject
- campaign through your carers' group or local voluntary
  organisation
- ask your local council for voluntary service to start up a
  campaign
- send evidence of poor treatment to national voluntary
  organisations

Other sources of information and help

- *The Disability Rights Handbook* (see page 126), available from
  the Disability Alliance, lists detailed information about rights,
  benefits and services. *Proper Channels* by Lydia Sinclair (see
  page 127), a practical guide to complaints about medical
  treatment, is available from MIND. MIND also produces a
  series of rights guides and advice leaflets.

Other useful organisations

For initial advice, go to your local law centre or citizens advice
bureau. They should be listed in the phone book. The law
centre can put you in touch with a local solicitor and advise you
about legal aid.

If you want to find your own solicitor, try the library which
should keep a copy of the *Solicitors' Regional Directory* which lists
local solicitors and what they do. Before going to talk to a

solicitor check what charges will be made for an initial
consultation.

There are also some national organisations that may be
helpful (see pages 129–33 for addresses);

- Action for the Victims of Medical Accidents (AVMA) advises
  victims of medical accidents on their rights and refers them to
  solicitors if legal action is possible. AVMA maintains a panel
  of medical experts who are prepared to give independent
  opinions, as well as a panel of solicitors with wide experience
  in this field.
- The College of Health campaigns on behalf of patients, works
  to bring about improvements in health care services and in
  communications with patients, and maintains a register of
  self-help groups and voluntary organisations connected with
  health.
- The Patients Association aims to promote and protect the
  interests of patients and offers an advice service and a
  collective voice for patients. It is an independent organisation.
  It does not give medical advice but can give information on
  how to find a self-help group, how to change your doctor,
  how to follow through a complaint. The Patients Association
  and the College of Health have collaborated with Thames TV
  to produce *The Health Directory* (Bedford Square Press) which
  lists around 1,000 organisations set up to help patients and
  families with health problems.

Even if you do not have complaints, you may recognise ways of
improving services. Send your suggestions to the Community
Health Council, to a social services manager or to the Family
Practitioner Committee (whichever is appropriate).

Finally, there may be occasions when you want to express
your satisfaction with a service. If you are pleased with the
service you have received, tell the workers concerned and write
to the manager if you have the time. This is a great boost to
staff morale and may mean the service is made more widely
available to other carers.

Part III
Surviving the Day-to-Day

12 Managing a routine

It comes home to you very early on that it has got to be done, there is no way round it. The routine just becomes part of the day.

Does your daily routine work for both of you?

If you are caring every day over some time, things will start to fall into a routine which makes the day more easy to manage. As much of daily caring involves a series of nursing and domestic tasks that cannot be avoided, this is often the best way to cope. But the kind of routine you create can make a great difference to the quality of your lives together. Sometimes it feels like never-ending drudgery. As one carer said, 'I wake up in the morning thinking I'm going to do the same thing today as I did yesterday and I'm going to do tomorrow.'

The sheer hard work of the daily routine can make it difficult to carry on, and frustration and resentment starts to set in.

If you feel like this, it is time to take things in hand. This is how Alice copes: 'If I feel down I get the breakfast, do the necessary chores and go back to bed – feeling rather mischievous at myself. I don't stay long, but it works. I do not want any resentment to build up so by being as kind as I can to *me* there is none.'

You may already be too tired to see how you can make any changes. If so, try to enlist the help of someone to review your situation with you. While a routine gives structure and is probably helpful to the person you care for, it need not be without variety.

A routine is more likely to work and keep you both happy if you can arrange to:

● take breaks from each other – to go shopping, visit friends,

- enjoy leisure and social activities for both together *and* separately
- build in the active involvement of the person you look after in carrying out daily tasks (however small) – a physiotherapist or occupational therapist may be able to advise

Can you cut corners?

Perhaps you feel that you do not have time to do the things listed above. If so, are there ways you can simplify your household chores? For example:

- *Shopping.* Organise your shopping lists in groups of items you can get conveniently locally perhaps twice weekly and things that a neighbour would get you on a regular basis with his or her trip to the supermarket.
- *Household equipment.* Reliable machinery makes life easier such as a vaccuum cleaner, fridge/freezer, washing machine, microwave, etc. If you do not have these things you may be able to get a grant to buy them either from the Independent Living Fund or the Family Fund (see pages 69–70) or, if you are receiving income support, you may be eligible for a community care grant. Contact your local Department of Social Security.
- *Clothes.* Gradually replace clothes with ones that will drip or tumble dry so you can cut down on ironing.
- *Cut down.* Try living with the muddle for a while. Turn a blind eye to the dust and put your feet up for five minutes.

There may be all kinds of ways your home could be adapted to make nursing easier, or there may be aids and equipment that could help you. An occupational therapist can arrange this for you. You can also get advice about what aids are available from the Disabled Living Foundation (see page 131). Private suppliers will be listed in your Yellow Pages phone book and should give you an opportunity to try gadgets and appliances. You should not buy anything without trying it first.

Breaking up the day

If you and the person you care for are at home all day, the days may seem very long. Sometimes the same routine can become boring for you both, so this is how one carer copes:

To overcome the boring routine we often turn our day upside down and watch all the chat shows in the morning. Some are very informative and geared to our problems and then I do the chores after lunch.

There are various schemes which may be useful for occupying time during the day:

- Check with your library to find out if they run a service which will come to your home. You may be able to borrow cassettes and records, too.
- Some voluntary organisations run lending schemes for games, jigsaws, etc.
- Toys for young children with special needs may be lent through a toy library. To find your nearest one, contact Play Matters (see page 132).
- For people who are mentally active, the Open University runs courses designed for your needs.

When you are spending a lot of time in each other's company it is not unusual for anger and frustration to build up between you. This is only natural when you are both coping with very testing situations. As one carer said, 'You're under so much pressure that sometimes you don't like the person you love because of the things they do.'

If you feel you are both getting stuck in a rut, you may benefit from time apart during some part of the week. Check with your local social services to see if there is any day care that your relative would enjoy attending. This might be:

- a day centre
- a day hospital
- a work centre/sheltered workshop
- an education and training centre

Places are often in short supply and transport can be a problem. The person you look after may also need time to adjust to the change, but gradually you can work up to a situation that suits you both. As Mrs Scott found:

My husband was persuaded to attend a day centre one day a week which gave me a free day: later he attended two days a week and I returned to business one day. Through social services I took a short Open University course, without expense, on 'Caring for Older People'.

'We never know what will happen next'

For some carers, it is the *lack* of a routine that is the problem. If you are looking after someone with unpredictable moods and behaviour you may find the constant disorganisation makes life very difficult, particularly if you are trying to run a household to meet other peoples' needs as well.

After 12 years, Mr and Mrs Jenkins have learnt to cope with the difficulties of caring for their son who has been diagnosed schizophrenic. But, as Mrs Jenkins says, 'The bad days take some getting through and we know to tell the social worker or doctor if we have a bad patch.'

Mrs Jenkins listed the things that have helped her manage the unpredictable daily routine:

1 We never get up expecting the day to be simple – just a challenge.
2 I try, above all else, to keep calm.
3 We avoid blaming ourselves for any aspect of the problem – it's only human but doesn't help.
4 We try not to be antagonistic towards our son. He can't help it and we want to stay friends and keep his trust.
5 We have simplified our life and particularly all essential chores.
6 Precious ornaments are packed away in the back of a wardrobe.
7 We don't risk problems over money or essential papers. We keep them all together and hide them. Similarly with keys. Anything to reduce our worries and make us feel more in control of a situation (which we can never be completely).
8 We keep our sanity with other interests like reading, even occasionally.
9 Very importantly, we seek out meetings with other similar people.
10 We no longer expect doctors, social workers or whoever to know more than us about the problems. They don't always, and it can help some discussions to keep a careful log of symptoms.

Another carer, who looked after her husband who suffered from Alzheimer's Disease, listed her own ways of coping:

1 I altered my attitude, recognising he was ill, not just being difficult.
2 I tried not to argue – change the subject gently, without confrontation.
3 Encouraged him to discuss his symptoms, he was very frightened and needed reassurance.

4 We would sit and hold hands: physical contact was comforting for us both.

5 I used a small portable tape recorder with songs and music he used to love. They caught his attention and relaxed him (and me).

6 I enlisted the help of relatives and friends to talk to him on the telephone at regular times.

7 I tried not to feel guilty when I broke down under the stress.

8 I warned all neighbours, shopkeepers, fellow church-goers of the situation. People were kind and helpful once they grasped what was happening.

9 I got out of the house at least one hour a week. I contacted the local branch of the Alzheimer's Disease Society and got help: a lifeline to sanity.

10 I saw the GP on my own so that I could tell him everything.

11 I hid: the car ignition key, all interior door keys (in case he locked himself in), all exterior door keys (in case he wandered off) – as well as the electric kettle and lead.

12 When he wandered, I followed at a distance to see where he went. This gave me a clue where to look. Asked neighbours to be alert if they saw him 'take off'.

13 I kept a running commentary going about what I was doing (unless it upset him). I asked his help and advice, so he still felt a part of my life. I avoided ridicule when he said daft things.

14 I kept alcoholic drinks locked up, or else put Ribena in the sherry bottle and left the cupboard unlocked. He either went off it or carried on swigging without harm when I wasn't looking. I also locked away medicines.

15 I learnt to be a 'liar'. If he asked for his mother, who was dead for years, I tended to say she was out shopping rather than shock him with the truth.

16 I used meals-on-wheels occasionally to save effort – otherwise I prepared quick and simple meals.

17 I found out about help available: attendance allowance, carers' groups and so on. But I was so imprisoned, I had to ask a friend to go to the DSS for me. Also the church helped.

18 I called 'help!' when I needed it.

Working out your own guidelines can help with the day-to-day routine, but it is often hard to plan ahead, as the crises that arise can be so unexpected. As Jamal found out one day:

He would eat or drink anything in sight, so I made sure all medicines and harmful substances were locked away. I was driven to distraction when one bank holiday weekend I found the cat's tape worm pill had disappeared. The vet assured me it would have no ill effect.

Handing over to a helper

It is sometimes possible to get a break by bringing in a helper to your home. A clear daily routine can make it easier to hand over the care to a helper for a time. Patricia Slack describes how this can work in practice in her excellent book *Sweet Adeline* (co-written with her husband, Frank Mulville; see page 127). She describes how she evolved a method of care for her mother which meant she was still able to continue working but was also able to ensure her mother remained as independent, and as well cared for as was possible, until her death:

Because my mother could not explain her routine or what she wanted and a new helper was not yet familiar enough to understand her efforts to communicate, I always demonstrated the routine of washing and dressing and of undressing and going to bed.

She wrote down the daily routine, itemising those personal preferences which make the day go smoothly: 'Often my mother's protests were associated with failure in her routine – her hankie was not in her wheelchair, her tea was in the wrong cup or had sugar in it, or she wanted to watch a particular programme.' She would stay and watch until she was sure the helper understood how to lift and move her mother properly and how to splint her knee and help her to walk. The most difficult part was to persuade helpers of the importance of involving her mother in the chores. It helped to have a written routine to refer to. The routine was updated from time to time but this is one of the early ones.

8 am approximately. Up to commode; dentures in; sit up in bed. Mug of tea in china mug with carnation, plenty of milk and no sugar. One tablet prednisolene.
8.30–9 am Breakfast. Large plate of porridge with a spoon of sugar and two dessertspoons bran and plenty of milk, followed by two cups of tea in white cup and saucer.
9 am–10 am Out to commode, then onto wheelchair covered in white towel and wash down; also rub bottom, clean vest weekly, clean pants daily, and different sets of clothing at least every other day. If cold, warm jumper and cardigan or blouse, pullover and cardigan. Brushes own hair and likes to help make the bed. Keeps her hankie and table napkin tucked beside her in wheelchair.
10 am–1 pm Dries up breakfast dishes. Likes to squeeze out small items of washing. Likes to help make pastry and to watch cooking

preparations. Short walk in sitting room; exercise arm by polishing the table. Likes to go to the shops in wheelchair – she carries the housekeeping purse. Puzzles or games – will do puzzles on own if set out for her. Enjoys game of draughts, snakes and ladders or snap. Cups of tea or coffee. If coffee, takes one spoon sugar.

1 pm–2 pm Lunch and lavatory.

2 pm–4 pm Sometimes short sleep in chair or on bed. Out for walk, shopping or visitors. If warm, can sit in garden or just inside garage if breezy. Put on coat and hat – keep well wrapped up.

4 pm Tea – two cups, scone or slice of cake.

5.30 pm Lavatory. Likes to help wash up and prepare supper.

6–7 pm Supper.

8.30 pm Turn on electric blanket and fire (if cold).

9.30–10 pm Undress: commode; one tablet prednisolene, two teaspoons laxative if constipated. Dentures out; into bed. Lies on left side. Rub bottom; clothes well up and tucked round; cradle over sheet and under blanket. Likes hankie and table napkin under pillow. Turn off electric blanket; leave door ajar. Turn on baby alarm on the landing before you go to bed.

Television

Likes soap operas: Coronation Street, Dallas, Emmerdale Farm, Crossroads, family films, cooking, gardening, nature, news.

Weekly

To day hospital for speech therapy Wednesday mornings about 10.30 am.

Hoover and dust – general cleaning.

Shop for everyday items – if running low on tea and sugar etc.

Keep a list for supermarket – I do a big store shop every so often.

Hand wash my mother's personal clothing in Stergene – nightie, vest, pants and trousers. I'll wash other woollies.

Household washing – change tea cloths, towels and one sheet and pillow case each week. Gladys will take washing to launderette.

Ironing.

Likes and dislikes

My mother likes plain food – liver, chops, stew, roast, chicken or fish, green and root vegetables and boiled potatoes; salad; soup; beans on toast, scrambled eggs, poached egg, bacon and sausage.

Dislikes highly seasoned food such as curry. Does not like much gravy, no chips or processed food such as hamburgers or fish fingers.

Does not usually eat puddings but may have mashed banana or ice cream.

(From Patricia Slack and Frank Mulville, *Sweet Adeline: A Journey through Care*, pages 107–8, Macmillan Education, 1988.)

Review your own routine

If you are able to talk and discuss your situation with the
person you look after, try sitting down together and writing out
your routine. Use it as an exercise to discuss what you both
need to feel happy in your circumstances. If you cannot do this
together, try getting together with a friend to discuss it. Use
Patricia's routine as a model and include:

- your daily timetable – include personal details
- weekly events/chores
- likes and dislikes

You will probably be surprised to see how much you do in a
week. When you have written it out, try answering these
questions:

- Are you happy with the way you are doing things together?
- Are there chores that could be shared with other people or
  cut down?
- Would someone be able to take over from you by using this
  routine in the event of an emergency, or because you needed
  a break? What else would they need to know – e.g. telephone
  numbers, names of close family etc?
- Are there times in the day or week that are particularly
  difficult for you? If so, can you plan your time differently or
  get help?

Looking ahead

It can be hard looking into the future, especially if the condition
of the person you care for is variable and could change at any
time. But do bear in mind that caring over a long period of time
can be exhausting and what may seem easy to manage one
week may become a nightmare a month or two years later. You
must apply for all the benefits you can and organise to take
breaks before you become too tired.

Perhaps you both want to go away together. You can get
information about holidays that cater for people who are
disabled and their families from the Holiday Care Service (see
page 140). They can also help to arrange financial assistance.

Try to talk together with the person you care for to make
plans for taking time off. You may start with just a few hours a
week or you might start to introduce a relief carer gradually,
giving everyone time to get to know each other.

The only way to cope with long-term caring is to have breaks.

Even modest ones are hard to take because, as George says,
'You're continually listening and watching all the time. If you
just go out to peg out the washing, at the back of your mind,
you're wondering if she's all right.' But even though he does
not stop worrying, he manages to get away twice a week to visit
a friend. 'Those two hours a week are my lifeline.' His wife is
now starting at a day centre and they have both agreed to
overnight stays at an annex to the centre to let George get some
rest.

13 Changing relationships

Taking on the work of two people

If you are looking after someone who has a progressive illness, you are probably having to take on more and more of the responsibilities of running a household. Learning to cook or to balance the accounts involves energy and effort on top of the work you already do. As Mr Harris explains,

At the age of 68 I suddenly found myself running a home and looking after an invalid for 24 hours in every day. The first realisation was how useless I was. Imagine reaching that age without being able to cook, wash or iron linen or clean the house.

You may feel under some obligation to hide the effort that is involved with these new responsibilities so that the person you look after does not feel a nuisance or a burden. It is natural to want to protect that person from the too obvious realisation that their faculties are failing. Sometimes, though, this can work the other way. Keeping up a brave front can sometimes make a person even more dependent because your partner or relative no longer feels involved in daily decisions and may also find it hard to talk about feelings of lost independence and fears for the future.

When Edie was told that her mother had cancer, she found herself in a dilemma because the hospital had decided not to let her mother know of the diagnosis. From that point on, Edie says,

I found I was leading my mum's life for her – she had a lot of outside interests and I used to help her with them, so I was trying to keep her life going for her, because I knew that she had cancer and that was terrible for me. She was convinced that sooner or later she would be back to a normal life. In the end the strain was so much for me that I wrote to ask the hospital to tell my mother. They wouldn't do it because they said she was the type that couldn't take it, but I felt differently. We had always been close but the strain of those last six months was terrible: I think it was the first time we ever argued.

Situations like this are very hard to resolve. Unfortunately the views of relatives are not always considered important, but *you* are in many ways the expert. You know how a person close to you will respond and there are times when you may want to challenge medical opinion. This can be easier with the help and support of a close friend or somebody from a local support group to speak on your behalf.

Changing places

Looking after a parent can involve carrying out intimate nursing tasks which can be embarrassing for you both. You may feel your roles have reversed: that you are now 'parent' to your parent. How you manage this will obviously depend on your previous relationship with your parent. Sometimes caring for a parent is a satisfying way of repaying the care received in childhood. But this is not a standard equation: many illnesses demand care and nursing which is quite different from child-rearing.

Even between people who previously got along well together, there are times when the strain of caring becomes too much. Clare, a mild mannered and sensitive woman, told me, 'I just got to the point where I didn't want to be left alone with mum. I just felt I wanted to kill her.' People who have cared for a long time with little thanks or recognition do sometimes describe their feelings as 'murderous'.

Very often they are left to cope with an impossible situation: there may be very little support available, but keeping quiet about it will not bring help. If you are feeling trapped and unhappy, do try and find someone to talk to (see chapter 4) who might be able to help you find ways of easing the strain.

Other children in the family

Many people care for an impaired or ailing relative as well as looking after young children. Children are usually very aware of what is going on, but need to feel involved. Clear and honest explanations can avoid misunderstandings. Some children can secretly harbour fears that an illness or mishap in the family is somehow their fault. It is important to foster an atmosphere where the child can ask questions and express feelings.

Feelings will obviously be more complex if the ill person is a parent. Children will need to find their own ways of expressing sadness, love and anger.

The rage may be hard to contain, as one small boy, whose mother was dying of leukaemia, said: 'If leukaemia was a man, I'd punch his head in.' A terminal illness hits the whole family, but a comforting compensation can be talking with each other, as this boy's father said: 'We had to talk and we shared a lot of close moments which we might not have had otherwise.'

It can be very hard to know how to fairly divide one's love and attention when you are bringing up other children alongside a child with special needs. Some parents feel their other children suffer by having to mature early and feel a constant sense of guilt at not doing enough for one or other of the children. The best source of support for parents is usually with a support group of parents in a similar situation. Other children in the family benefit from these, too, as many will organise outings and events to cater for everyone's needs.

Most children will respond to your honesty and love, but sometimes a child may become very withdrawn or aggressive. If you are worried about your child you may be able to enlist the help of a teacher or welfare officer. Try talking to other parents at a support group, or you can be put in touch with local help by contacting: National Association of Young People's Counselling and Advisory Services (see page 132).

Between partners

Sudden illness can bring about major upheavals in a marriage or a partnership. Sometimes it is very hard to talk about what is happening.

Alan and Mary had been married for more than 40 years when Alan discovered he had cancer of the bladder. Alan found it hard to discuss his illness and fears with Mary and tried to put on a brave face so she would not worry. As the months went by Mary came to the conclusion that he no longer cared about her and became increasingly distressed. Eventually they sought help for the breakdown in their relationship. Mary learned that Alan cared for her deeply and was withdrawn because of his fear of being a burden to her. Alan learned that, in fact, he was not a burden at all and that he did not have to maintain a brave face.

Some illnesses may mean you are not able to talk together.

This is a lonely time, but communication need not stop completely. Lola explains: 'For those five years we had no conversation because Victor couldn't talk. But if something cropped up that took us back to the days before, I'd look at him and he'd look at me and we had a good old grin.'

For some people, it is the loss of sharing a life together that is the hardest. As Mrs See explains:

My husband is now like a spoilt child. I am cast in the role of mother – he wants me with him all the time but to fuss him, nurse him and wait on him hand and foot. Our sex life was good and fulfilled: all that is now gone, and it is devastating to think at 50 odd that is it for the rest of one's life.

A sense of one's own sexuality is interwoven with how you see yourself: your sense of who you are, how you feel about your body and how you value yourself. In a relationship where sexual contact has been very important, this change can be very unsettling and can make both partners feel that part of their identity has gone.

This may not be permanent. Loss of interest in sex is a common result of being unwell or tired. Although people may not feel able to have sex together there is still the need, perhaps more so than ever, for the expression of support and love. Physical closeness is important at these times; just to be held and cuddled can give reassurance that words cannot give.

Sometimes, the change of roles that Mrs See describes above, where she has become 'mother' to her husband, is irreversible. Taking on the personal care of another may also affect your sexual feelings for him or her.

Other couples find different ways of sharing intimacy:

We did try to sleep in the double bed together, but each time I turned it hurt him so we sleep separately. But we enjoy the feeling of being near to each other and I am there if he needs me. We exchange comments on our dreams as we both seem to have funny and vivid dreams. We often have a cuddle. A kiss is a must – when we first wake up and last thing at night and if I am going out.

Specialist counsellors can discuss sexual difficulties with individuals or couples (see pages 21–2 for how to contact a counsellor). There are also some specialist organisations that may be able to help (see pages 129–30):

- the Association to Aid Sexual and Personal Relationships of People with a Disability (SPOD) provides an information, advisory and referral service for disabled clients, and information and training for professional workers

- Relate Marriage Guidance Council can put you in touch with local counsellors. Be prepared for a waiting list
- Brook Advisory Centres have clinics in various cities, providing confidential advice on sexual problems for young people
- the Lesbian and Gay Switchboard (tel. 071-837 7324) has a 24-hour advisory and counselling service run by lesbians and gay men
- the AIDS Helpline (0800 567 123) provides a free national advice service on HIV/AIDS

14 Living with loss

I appear as if I am coping well but I do not feel I am inside. It is like walking a tightrope.

Loss of an 'ordinary life'

Many carers experience powerful feelings of loss and grief which can be as hard to handle as an actual bereavement. Because caring is so often carried out in isolation, without proper emotional support and practical assistance, carers may suffer losses on all fronts: loss of independence, social life, employment and access to a decent income.

For parent carers, the sense of loss may be experienced as a loss of potential – however much they love their child there will always be the pain of knowing that their child with special needs cannot participate in everyday life as fully as other children. This may be because of physical limitations imposed by the child's condition, but is made worse by the way our society is organised. Disabled children and adults suffer daily problems in ordinary living because transport, housing and public places are not designed to include them. Limitations inevitably extend to other children in the family: taking a young family on an outing with a child who is disabled may mean negotiating stairs and escalators (with a buggy) while keeping an eye out for the other children. Sometimes the effort involved means parents give up trying.

Carers also grieve on behalf of the people they care for. The bond of empathy and love for the other person is often strong and it is painful to witness the suffering of someone you care for, even though you are doing all you can to make life easier in practical ways.

If the person you care for has been active and independent before their illness of impairment, there will probably be a long period of adjustment when he or she will experience feelings of rage and frustration. As the carer, you will probably be at the receiving end and you may feel that you can't do anything right. In a sense, this is true, because what an ill or newly disabled person wants – health and wholeness – is something you do not have the power to give. Just as you may need the support of other carers in a similar position to you, it is important for the person you look after to have peers who can encourage and understand his or her difficulties.

A 'bereavement without a burial'

I feel I have lost the man I loved and who loved me.

If you are not able to communicate with the person you look after, or if the illness has inflicted brain damage, you may feel sadness on your own behalf as well as for the person you care for: sometimes this feeling can be there in every detail of daily life. In addition you may have lost the personal support of a previously close partner and will have to take on more and more practical tasks in the home. Mrs Vee looks after her husband who is suffering from slow deterioration of mental and physical faculties that is a result of Alzheimer's Disease. She says:

I am told I have suffered a 'bereavement without a burial'. I find I cannot reach him – I do not know what he understands, what he suffers. I am told it is a blessing that he is not aware of what has happened – but I understand. I am very lonely now: for the first time in 50 years there is no one to turn to, to laugh with.

If you recognise your own situation in this, you can help yourself by recognising also that you are likely to be experiencing grief, which is a reaction to losing important aspects of a relationship in your life, *even if* that person is still alive. This can make great demands on your emotional and physical ability to cope.

Understanding grief

We all come to terms with loss in our own way and there is no standard measure, but grief may be expressed in the following ways:

- Yearning: sudden pangs of loss and wanting happier times to return can be jogged by a memory, a photograph or can just arrive unexpectedly at any moment.
- Fear and anxiety: memories of former losses or periods of distress can re-awaken old childhood fears as well as new fears connected to an uncertain future.
- Anger: feelings of helplessness in the face of illness and possible death can generate anger at what has happened and the injustice of lost opportunity. It may be further fuelled by lack of understanding from others.
- Guilt: with a late diagnosis of an incurable condition, it is common to feel guilty about past behaviour and to feel that 'if only I had known' I would have been more patient, understanding, etc. Difficulty in accepting a diagnosis may lead to a feeling of somehow being responsible for causing it.
- Lack of self-confidence: severe illness and death are often taboo subjects, which can make it hard for the carer to feel comfortable about sharing worries and daily concerns because other people may be embarrassed. The carer can also experience a loss of his or her own sense of identity when all the attention and focus falls to the person who is ill.

If you are experiencing any of these reactions you need to:

- *Share your fears with someone.* (You may wish to turn to 'Finding someone to talk to' on page 20–2.)
- *Take extra care of yourself.* Try to eat well even if your appetite is low. Try to rest and take exercise. Be gentle with yourself.
- *Talk together.* If appropriate to your situation, do try to keep talking together about what is happening. If you are caring for someone who is dying it is best to prepare practically and emotionally. It is not morbid to talk about death if you are able to.
- *Widen your circle.* It is tempting to withdraw into isolation with private pain, but it is important for both of you to stay in touch with as many people as you can. If old friends don't understand, try to seek out a support group (see chapter 9).
- *Tackle your guilt.* Is it other people's expectations that make you feel guilty? Put the blame where it belongs. If you are not receiving enough help to feel adequate to the task, it may be because services are poor in your area. But the human need to find a cause or a reason for illness can also cause guilt because we sometimes mistakenly blame ourselves. If you feel you are to blame for illness it may help to read Jean's story below.

Jean's story: overcoming guilt

Four-year-old Emily was being treated successfully for leukaemia but her mother, Jean, suffered intense feelings of guilt that she had in some way been responsible for her daughter's illness.

Perhaps she had allowed Emily to eat too much junk food, or maybe they should not have bought a house near such a busy road where the air was so polluted. Could the damage have been done even earlier, while Jean was pregnant with Emily? She did not smoke and she had only had the occasional glass of wine, but might she have passed something on to Emily which gave her the leukaemia?

The answer to all these questions is 'no'. Leukaemia is one of many cancers where little is known about the cause, but it was not enough for Jean to be told that she was not responsible. She needed to be able to work it out for herself.

During a series of counselling sessions she was asked to make a list of all the factors she thought might have caused Emily's illness. She rated these, according to how likely they were, on a scale of one to ten. In doing this she was asked to recall everything she had heard or read about leukaemia and its possible causes. Did she know of any evidence to support any of her theories about why Emily had got the disease? Was there anything she could have done to prevent it?

Slowly, Jean began to accept that she was not to blame. In fact, she had been very quick to realise when Emily was first ill and to take her to the doctor. Blaming herself was not going to help Emily, but encouraging her through the often unpleasant treatment for her leukaemia would.

It is very hard living with constant uncertainty when you do not know whether the condition of the person you care for will improve. This is why a clear diagnosis and detailed medical advice is so important, and it can make such a difference to have a doctor you feel able to talk to and ask questions. Sadly, the stress and uncertainty can put a great strain on personal relationships, and many marriages and partnerships break down under the strain imposed by caring responsibilities.

The frustration of caring can be unbearable sometimes. As

Mary said, 'I get so frustrated I shout and swear at him. I feel terrible about it but I can't help it.'

Carers who have come to terms with loss

Strangely enough, it often seems to be just at the point that you accept the loss in your life that the caring starts to become a little easier. Lola was insistent with her doctor that she should know the truth about her husband's chances after his second stroke. Although she had to live for two years with the knowledge that he might die at any moment, she said, 'I think on the whole it was better to know. You know it's all downhill from there on, somehow you build an inner strength.'

Once the period of shock is over, some carers talk of discovering new strengths. The challenge of illness and death can give life a new perspective. Priorities change as some things lose their importance and others gain. The valuable things in your life can suddenly stand out in stark relief, and this can bring people closer together. Each day becomes more precious and a positive attitude (which does not deny problems) can help you to take each day as it comes.

The sadness and the grief do not go away, but a hard-won adjustment to change and to personal loss is what enriches the lives of some carers:

Beulah was born in 1953. I am now 57 years old and I can honestly say I would not have missed a day of Beulah's life. She has given me so much love and happiness.

We've had to learn to talk together much more as a family. Looking after Greg has brought a bond that wasn't there before.

Now that I no longer blame my wife for things she cannot help doing, her temper tantrums have ceased. The house is now full of fun and laughter. When her emergency bell rings, I might find myself saying, 'What the hell does she want now?' but I give no sign of that to her (and only reluctantly to you).

I have to learn to trust others, even if my daughter cannot. I lead a full life doing voluntary work and caring for her. She makes my life fuller. We, as a family, love, respect and honour her. It could have happened to any one of us, so we live each day expecting anything and hoping that our caring will not be found wanting.

15 Finding a long-stay home for an elderly person

My husband is now in a nursing home. He is in my thoughts every second of the day, but I know it is right for him to be there. I feel no guilt, only sadness.

There may come a time when looking after your relative at home is no longer in the best interests of you or the other person. It is a difficult time for all concerned. For the person in need of care, it can mean having to face up to increasing physical frailty and loss of independence. As the carer, you will probably be concerned with whether the care will be as good as yours. As Lola said, 'You begin to feel nobody can look after them as well as you do, and I wanted him with me as long as I could have him.'

You will want to discuss the situation with your doctor and other professional staff such as a social worker or community nurse. They will be able to tell you what your options are. As well as talking with your relative and partner about the future, other members of the family will also need to be consulted. There may still be other alternatives you have not considered, but if not, the family should be aware of the financial implications of residential care. A long stay may use up all the savings, if there are any, and this needs to be discussed at the outset.

Even if you are not both ready to take this step just now it is important to be prepared for the future. In many areas there are waiting lists for this kind of housing. Sometimes it is possible for an elderly person to attend a day centre attached to the home, or you may be able to arrange visits to familiarise your relative with the new surroundings before taking the final step.

Moving house is a stressful event for all of us, particularly for an old person who may feel the additional loss of privacy and freedom, but there are ways to make this time easier. It is important for you to remain positive and to continue to value the care you have already given: try not to view passing on the care as failure. You have done what you can and it will help the person moving into care if you can look at the move with optimism.

The move does not mean the end of your caring, but it will take on a different aspect. Some carers describe this as 'quality time' and find that when the strain of the physical work is handed over, they are able to devote themselves to giving love and support to their relative or partner:

My mother's last six months in the home were a good time for me, because I was able to visit her regularly and just be with her and do nothing at all and we felt good together because I wasn't the focus of her anger any more. She could complain about other people who were failing her . . . so from my point of view *not* looking after her was better than being there full time.

What alternatives are there?

You will already have worked through all the help available in Part II. Sometimes the smallest adaptations to the old person's home can make the world of difference: raising plug sockets, installing time switches, using calendars and reminders.

Sheltered accommodation

The other alternative to caring for an elderly person yourself is sheltered accommodation. This is a kind of halfway house between living at home and residential care. They are usually independent flats or bungalows with some communal grounds and living areas. The elderly person will still need to be fairly independent as wardens, while willing to keep a watchful eye, will not usually expect to actually help with caring tasks. Help from social services and other support is still available just as if people were living in their own homes. Some voluntary organisations run their own sheltered accommodation to cater for particular cultural or religious needs. Others are for people who have had some link with a particular profession, such as the Armed Forces.

To find out about sheltered accommodation in your area, contact your local housing department. There is often a waiting list but places are also allocated according to need.

Some sheltered housing is for sale. You can get a list of

companies from the New Homes Marketing Board, 82
Cavendish Street, London W1M 8AD.

What kinds of homes are there?

There are two kinds of homes for elderly people:

Residential care homes are suitable for elderly people who can no
longer live at home and need some help with getting up,
washing and so on, but who do not need skilled nursing care.
They are also referred to as rest homes, old people's homes or
(for social services homes) 'Part III homes'. Homes looking after
more than three people must be registered with the social
services department. Do not use an unregistered home.

Nursing homes are suitable for people who need nursing care
and are staffed by qualified nurses and sometimes a doctor in
attendance. By law, they must be registered. Most nursing
homes are run privately: there are very few in the NHS.

Sometimes a home is 'dual registered', which means it is
allowed to operate both as a residential care home *and* a
nursing home.
   Homes can be run by:

- your local authority (the social services department)
- an individual or company as a private business
- a voluntary organisation (or charity) on a non-profit making
  basis, usually set up to cater for particular groups of people,
  e.g. of a particular faith or retired from a particular profession

How do you find out about them?

Social services homes

Application should be made through your local social services
office, not to the individual home. A social worker will probably
visit to assess the needs of the elderly person and to find out
about the financial position, state of health and so on. It is
useful to have the support of your family doctor to back you up
in your application. Places are limited and you may have a long
wait. If you do not hear anything for several months, contact the
social services office to remind them you are still looking for a
place.

Private and voluntary homes

Standards will vary between homes and price does not always reflect quality. At the time of writing, application should be made to the individual home. The procedure may be different in 1991, when changes in the law come into effect. You may then have to go through the social services department. Before making your choice, visit several homes and use the checklist below to help you make your choice. Ask people you know: personal recommendation from someone who knows the home may be the most useful information. You should check that the home is registered. This means that a residential care home is registered by the local social services department and is inspected by them at least twice a year. Nursing homes are registered by the district health authority. A registration certificate must be displayed at the home and you can check with the registering authority. You will find lists of homes by:

- contacting the registering department of social services or the health authority
- using the Yellow Pages: look under Residential and Retirement Homes or Nursing Homes
- asking a social worker at your local social services department or at the hospital if your relative is being nursed in hospital. He or she will be able to give you information but is not allowed to recommend individual homes. Social services also keep information on homes for people from religious or ethnic minorities.
- contacting the local Age Concern group
- contacting the citizens advice bureau

What to look out for when you visit a home

When you visit a home you will need to get a feel for how it is run. Whose needs come first: the home's or the resident's? How do the staff treat the residents? Are they seen as customers who deserve a good service? Remember that this is going to be a permanent home and your relative will want to retain as much control as possible over his or her daily life. Breakfast in bed may be nice on holiday, but having no choice is a different matter.

Here is a checklist to help you:

Essentials

- Is the home run by the local authority (social services), a private individual or a voluntary organisation?
- Is the home registered?
- There must be a brochure giving you full factual information about the home, the number and size of rooms, services provided, the scale of charges and a list of any additional charges not included in the fees.

First impressions

- Do you like the feel of the place? Does the atmosphere seem right for your relative?
- Do you like the way residents are treated? Talk to staff and to residents and watch how the staff talk to the residents.
- Is the home for men and women or for one sex only?
- Is the home near to public transport? (Think of the needs of visitors.)
- Is it near family and friends?
- Is it near to local shops?
- What is the ratio of staff to residents?
- What is the ratio of untrained staff to residents?
- Does the home have communal pets?
- Is there enough light and ventilation?

Facilities

Ask to look at all the rooms.

- Are there plenty of single rooms?
- Do they have their own hand basins?
- Do some have their own toilet and shower/bath?
- Are double rooms reserved for couples or close friends wanting to share?
- Are there any rooms which more than two people share? (If so the home is not obeying the code of practice.)
- Are there plenty of bathrooms and separate toilets?
- Are they within easy reach and equipped with lever-handled taps, grab rails and raised toilet seats?
- Are there aids to help people get on and off the toilet and in and out of the bath?
- Are the bathroom doorways wide enough for a wheelchair or walking aid to get through?

- Are the communal living and dining rooms large, pleasant and well furnished?
- Is there a TV set in the lounge or are the residents encouraged to have sets in their own rooms?
- Can residents bring their own furniture and decorate to their own taste?
- If not, are there individual cupboards and wardrobes in each room, and somewhere to lock valuables?
- Is there a good central heating system and can it be controlled individually in each room?
- Can residents lock their rooms and is privacy respected?
- Is there a lift or stair-lift?
- Are there handrails on the stairs and corridors?
- Are there ramps for wheelchairs for small inclines?

Visitors

- Can visitors come at any time?
- Can they stay overnight?
- Can residents entertain visitors in their own rooms, or is there a special visitors' sitting room?

Choice in routine

- Can residents choose when to take a bath?
- Can residents get up and go to bed when they like?
- Can residents eat in their own room if they wish?

Meals and mealtimes

- Is there a varied menu and a balanced diet? (Ask to see the menus for a week and, if possible, arrange to stay for a meal in order to try the food and service.)
- Does the home cater for vegetarian and religious diets?
- Can residents have cups of tea between meals if they want to?
- What times are meals served?

Activities

- Are outings and social events organised on a regular basis?
- Are residents encouraged to pursue hobbies or educational interests?

- Is there a residents' association they can join?
- Are they encouraged to do chores and to look after their own rooms if they wish?

Health and medical matters

- Is continuity with the residents' own doctors maintained?
- What arrangements are there for any regular medication that residents need if you or the resident decide it is necessary?
- Are they encouraged to keep and administer their own drugs, or are these kept in a safe place and handed out by the manager or matron?
- Is a careful record kept of dosages and times they are taken?
- Will the home allow residents to stay if and when they become very frail, or will they have to move to other accommodation?
- Is there a visiting chiropodist, physiotherapist and/or other professionals?

Financial and legal matters

- Do you know what the charges for 'extras' will be?
- Do residents receive a proper statement regularly with details of all items charged for?
- Does the home take control of pension books? This is not good practice: any arrangement should be between you and the resident.
- Are they covered for personal insurance?
- What are the conditions under which a resident's stay may be terminated on either side?
- Is there a clearly established complaints procedure?
- Are complaints handled in a satisfactory way?
- Does the home meet the necessary fire regulations and safety standards? (The registering authority should tell you who is responsible for checking this.)

When you have found a home that seems to be right for the person you care for, try to arrange a trial stay before making a final decision. (Adapted from Thames Television's *The Treatment: A Guide to Choosing an Old People's Home*.)

Caring at a distance

You may experience all kinds of reactions when your relative moves into long-term care. Relief can quickly give way to feelings of guilt, sadness and anger. You may feel you have let the person down by no longer looking after them at home, even though you know the task had become impossible. The enforced parting may arouse feelings of grief and hopelessness.

Any of these feelings are natural and should pass. In the meantime, talk to friends or, if you continue to feel concerned, talk to your doctor or social worker or a carers' support group.

Your support will still be needed by your relative during the time that he or she is adjusting to the new surroundings. The staff at the home should welcome your active involvement, for instance at meal times or during activities. Other members of the family can be encouraged to visit and, as time goes on, you may be able to take your relative on outings or for overnight stays, if this seems a good idea.

You may find you are thinking about your partner or relative a good deal – and maybe worrying about whether the standard of care is as good as yours. Try not to give yourself too hard a time: plan a few treats for yourself. You are probably still very tired and under some strain and it can take a while before you can feel full of energy again. In the meantime, you need to look after yourself and if you have been spending a long time looking after someone else, this may not be easy to do.

16 Death and bereavement

Today I shed a little more of the past. The van called at about 11.00 am and took the clothes I had offered them. I think that she would have been pleased to think that her clothes would be put to good use and not just slung out to jumble for all and sundry to toss about. How good that the day was hot and sunny, so I could go afterwards and sit by her fishpond, as she had done so many times when she was alive and gardening. I gazed at her marguerites and thought about her again.

After the death of someone close to you, you are likely to be given all sorts of conflicting advice from well-meaning friends and professionals about how to cope with bereavement. The only yardstick is, if it doesn't feel right, ignore it. Everyone is different in the way they adjust, and you must do what feels comfortable for you.

Mourning is an essential part of recovering from the shock of losing someone close to you and it is important to allow ourselves time to grieve. Sometimes it is hard to do this. There is often the whole family to consider, and sometimes consideration for others can inhibit the free expression of your own sadness. This is particularly true when a child dies.

The way you grieve will reflect your own personality, beliefs and culture; religious rituals and observances may be very important at this time. Even for people who do not have a religious faith, there may still be personal rituals that have meaning for you.

The grieving process

Even though everyone experiences grief in their own way there is a recognisable grieving process which has its own pattern.

This is not to say you progress logically through it or even that you will necessarily experience each stage. It is common to feel bouts of misery, anger, depression, peace and numbness all within one day. Such extremes may feel very difficult to manage but will gradually lessen in intensity.

Anniversaries or memories can trigger these feelings again long after a death. This may be painful but is quite normal and does not mean you are going through the whole process again.

The following is intended as a rough guide only to stages in the grieving process. Remember – your own experiences may be very different.

- *Shock and disbelief.* A sense of numbness and disbelief is often an initial reaction. It is a natural way of allowing you to feel the loss more slowly.
- *Expressions of grief.* Waves of painful realisation of the loss can be immobilising in their intensity at first. Some people express grief through anger and hostility which may be a way of dealing with feelings of helplessness. Others may be fixed in regrets about things that they should have said or done.
- *Depression and apathy.* Depression is a joyless state but it has a function. It may be a period of non-emotion, as a reaction to acute feelings of anxiety, guilt and anger. It may also happen when the realisation dawns that the person who has died cannot be brought back.
- *Signs of recovery.* Feelings of misery and pain start to give way. It becomes possible to keep the memory of the person who has died without experiencing the intense agony and bitterness of early grief.

You may experience grief by feeling nothing at all for a while, or you may be engulfed in strong emotions. Both are normal, but it is important to realise that you need to take care of yourself during this time, particularly if the bereavement leaves you living alone.

People who have been caring for a person for some time before they die may experience the death quite differently from other relatives. One carer explained, 'Some people said "you must cry" but I didn't need to. I'd done all my crying long before she died.'

When someone has been taken into long-term care, the process of bereavement may be a long and painful one.

I felt in a kind of limbo. I was free, but not free. I would visit every day, but she didn't know me any more and when she eventually died I hardly knew what I felt. But gradually the memories came back of her old self: warm hearted and generous to a fault.

For others, the separation of going into care can mean the bereavement is easier to manage: 'The enforced parting did, I think, make the bereavement less painful than it would have been had she died at home.'

Carers who feel they have given their care freely and that their caring has been worthwhile and successful may feel relieved and grateful that the person is released from pain. Carers who have been caring under considerable strain are also likely to feel relief, but in these circumstances the feeling of relief may be accompanied by guilt. For people who have been giving care on top of other family or work responsibilities, the dominant feeling may be a sense of freedom; and grief may take a while to make itself felt, as Helen explains,

At first it was sheer relief. It took about three months before the regrets started to come in. I started to realise that I was saving up little stories to tell Mother, and I didn't have anyone to tell anymore. Then I started to appreciate the good things about her that had been hidden from me while she was being so annoying! Remembering that she did have a good sense of humour, that she appreciated funny slips of the tongue.

For carers who have been struggling alone over many months or years, bereavement can bring a double loss: a loss of identity and purpose in the role of carer as well as a loss of the person. The habit of putting someone else's needs before one's own over a long time can be hard to abandon. Loss of a partner may feel devastating when every day has been devoted to that person's care. Suddenly, there is no motivation to shop, to eat or to look after oneself.

If, while caring, you have been bottling up emotions and living on the edge of exhaustion, you may be prone to physical symptoms or may start to feel emotions that have been repressed for a long time (see chapter 4).

Sadly, death often occurs when the carer has agreed to take a break, and this can often leave the carer with feelings of guilt:

Finally I was feeling so bad, I agreed with the doctor and health visitor to allow my husband to go to the General Hospital. They picked him up on Monday morning and it was all over by Friday afternoon. He went in and he'd given up. For months afterwards, I kept telling myself, if I hadn't let him go into hospital he'd still be with me. I know now that he didn't want to go on as he was.

Feelings of regret and of not having done enough for the person who has died can hold up the healing process after a bereavement. This is how Peter learnt to deal with it:

Peter's story

Peter was 22 when his mother died. He had shared the care with other members of his family but three years later was still feeling intensely guilty that he did not do more to help. He wished he had spent more time with her but hadn't realised just how ill she was. He frequently dwelt on his teenage rows, his thoughtlessness and the assumption that Mum would always be there to pick up the pieces. Now, he felt depressed, he was getting behind at work and there didn't seem to be much point to life.

Peter was persuaded to see a counsellor and to talk about his feelings of guilt. There was no denying he had been a difficult teenager, but what had he learned from this? At the time of his mother's death he had just finished training to be a draughtsman and had got a job with the local council. His mother would have been pleased and reassured by his progress, but disappointed that he was falling behind now.

Peter found it helpful to write a letter to his mother, explaining how he felt and describing his regrets about his earlier behaviour. By apologising formally in this way he felt more able to close the door on his difficult adolescence and look hopefully towards the future.

Some of the reactions to a death may seem alarming because they do not fit in with an idea about how you should feel. Some people describe a sense of hyper-reality and strength at the time of a death. When the body is in shock, it can produce a surge of adrenalin that can make you feel quite 'high'.

Habitual behaviour may take over: you can find yourself setting the table for the absent person as if they were still alive. These reactions are not unusual: it does not mean you are losing your grip, just that you need time to adjust.

You do not have to be feeling sad all the time; taking time to go out and to distract yourself does not mean you have forgotten the person. Sometimes your mind just needs a rest.

What needs to be done when a person dies

If you are looking after someone who is seriously ill, you may need to prepare yourself to cope with the practical side of a death. Talk it over with your doctor or hospice nurse, if you have one.

If a person dies at home, you must call your doctor who will sign a medical certificate unless he or she decides to refer the matter to the coroner.

If a person dies at hospital the doctor on duty will issue the certificate. This paper must be taken to the Registrar of Births and Deaths who will issue the death certificate and the notification of disposal which should be passed to the funeral director. You will probably need several copies of the death certificate: a copy each for the will, any pension claims, insurance policies and investments.

When the death certificate has been issued you will also be given a certificate authorising the funeral. The National Association of Funeral Directors (see page 132) has a code of practice approved by the Office of Fair Trading and members will give you an estimate of costs.

It helps to plan ahead if you can as it is not easy to make decisions at a time of loss and distress. You can ask for estimates in advance: it's a good idea to ask two different firms to quote so that you can compare costs.

Age Concern (see page 129) can advise you about advance payment for funerals. Families who have lost a child under 16 can get a free funeral service from the Co-Operative Society Funerals Service. Contact your nearest one for details (they are listed in the telephone book).

You can apply for help with funeral costs through the Social Fund. It is the financial circumstances of the applicant, not the deceased, that matters. To get help with the cost of a basic funeral you have to be getting income support, housing benefit or family credit and have savings below a certain level.

Take your time

Try not to be rushed into decisions. You may find your feelings change about such things as whether or not you want to see the body and what you want to do after the funeral.

After the chaotic activity that often accompanies the funeral, you may find that attention drops off suddenly. This is when you are likely to feel low. Try to ensure that you are going to have daily contact with someone for at least six weeks. If it is not possible to see someone, even for half an hour, it is reassuring to know that you will get a phone call at a fixed time. Don't be afraid to ask friends and relatives: they will probably be pleased to know how to help, and may not have offered because they feel embarassed or do not want to intrude.

If you feel you want to make contact with others who have gone through a similar experience, you might want to contact a voluntary organisation such as CRUSE, or for families who have lost a child, Compassionate Friends (see pages 130–1). Don't cancel any help you were having in the home until you are sure you do not need it for yourself. You may find that once you are able to let go that you feel very tired and need a bit of extra help for a while.

You may find yourself lacking in energy for everyday chores. You might just want to sit and cry or stare into space, or you might feel anxious, keep losing things or become forgetful. You may have bouts of sudden, inexplicable fear. These are very common feelings and can leave you feeling low and drained. Make sure you eat well and try to get some sleep. If you feel worried about it, talk to your doctor and a close friend.

Just when you start to feel better, you may find that small things can make you slip back to how you were feeling at the beginning. As time goes on, this will become less distressing. Take your time, if you can, over practical things. You will know when you are ready to sort out clothes and personal effects. As one carer explains, 'It has taken quite some strength of will to throw out letters, medical cards and other items to do with the "caring" days.'

Because everybody copes in a different way, a death in the family can sometimes create a rift between people: partnerships can go through a rough patch. It often helps for each person to have a friend outside the family to turn to for support – as well as each other. Children will also feel loss and sadness, and it helps if you can talk to them about what has happened. They may need to know that you feel the same way; by trying to protect them seeing your sadness, they can become more upset, not less. It can help all of you to go through it together.

It can seem as if you will never feel normal again. You will adjust. You won't forget the person, but you will find ways to bear the loss and to enjoy life again.

17 Resuming an independent life

I couldn't get used to not being needed by someone. I had to learn to be a part of the world again.

For some people, life is soon restored to a normal pattern after the responsibility for caring has ended. Grief may be tempered by the knowledge that you gave what help you could to the person close to you; and other commitments to friends, work and family may return you speedily to the flow of day-to-day life.

For others, this process may be very much more difficult. The physical and emotional strain of caring can make resuming an ordinary life very hard, quite apart from the process of bereavement. Here are a few common ways in which people adapt to their new situation. None are 'wrong' in any way, they are simply different styles of reacting to change – but there are pitfalls to watch for.

Retreating into isolation

When all services and contacts have revolved around the needs of the person being looked after, the carer can suddenly find him or herself alone in the home when the person goes into care or dies. The hustle and bustle of commodes, home help, district nurse, doctor and daily crises may have taken their toll, but their absence can be eery. The need for support may continue long after a death and many carers feel the need to continue to have somewhere 'to let off steam' as well as to find company and understanding. If this describes your own situation, do try to maintain contact with people.

You may feel you cannot use the support of a carers' group,

but there is no reason why you should not continue to meet people from the group informally even if you are no longer a carer. Some groups positively welcome the presence of 'ex-carers' who can bring a different perspective to the problems of 'new' carers.

You may find it hard to adapt to the quiet, the lack of a routine. Take one day at a time, but try to keep a few things planned for each day and week ahead, gradually building up your contacts, physical strength and outside interests. Think about getting away for a holiday if you can.

Making up for lost time

Some people want to get as far away from the whole business as they can. In Dervla Murphy's wonderful autobiography *Wheels within Wheels* she describes how she came to fulfil her life ambition after many years of arduous caring for her mother. She learnt how to use a shotgun, strapped a small bag to her bicycle and cycled from Ireland to India!

Most of us have less adventurous aspirations, but for many young carers in particular there may be an impatience to make up for lost time.

Try to be realistic about what you can achieve. Be prepared for setbacks: things don't always fall into place immediately. It is important for your own self-esteem that you continue to value the part of your life which was dedicated to caring. If you don't, nobody else will. Talk about it, describe what it involved in applications for jobs. Be proud of what you have done.

Taking up the care of someone else

After caring for a long time, life may suddenly seem empty and without purpose. Rather than experience the discomfort of the unknown, it may be tempting to return to familiar territory and to fill the gap with new responsibilities by looking after another relative who needs your care. This is fine if you know this is really what you want to do, but before getting too involved, try to stand back and ask yourself, 'Why?' Is it because you really want to? Is it because other people expect you to, or is it because you fear for your own future without caring for someone else?

Don't worry if you do not immediately feel full of confidence and energy. Trust yourself and give yourself time to find out what *you* need for a change. This will probably take some practice! In the meantime, plan a few treats and try to delay any decisions until you know you are ready to stand by them.

Other peoples' attitudes are likely to dictate how easy it is for you to resume the life that you would wish for. Employers, friends or relatives may understand the idea of grieving and bereavement, but there is less recognition of the rather more complex feelings after a long period of caring. If you are in employment, try not to be pressured back to work before you are ready. It is quite normal to need some time to recuperate, to reassess your life and to gather your strength to cope with the changes you are going through. In the following interview, Helen explains how she met some of the challenges that faced her after her mother died:

Helen

For a woman whose husband dies leaving her a widow it must be devastating: from being occupied 24 hours a day to having nothing. For me it was more like being let out of school – having the freedom to do things that I wanted to do. So certainly in the first year, there was a lot of enjoyment about being free of responsibility, but the other feelings – the bad feelings – are still there. A lot of things are still hidden, and five years on I'm beginning to forget how difficult it was and it is quite interesting to be reminded of it by talking to carers: all the anger and resentment is still there, still bubbling away.

When my mother died I had assumed that then suddenly everything would snap into position and I would start a full-time job – I would do all the things that were delayed whilst I had been looking after her. Of course I didn't because my back was very bad. I spent the first two years after she died going to different osteopaths trying to get my back right. I wasn't fit to do a job, I had to lie down for a couple of hours in the middle of every day.

Were you able to see friends again?

Helen

So many friends had full-time jobs and because we didn't have a car it was difficult unless they came to visit us . . . but we had other friends this end of town who were very good.

I also went out to make new friends. I got involved in CND and that was nice because it was a ready-made circle of people to make friends with and a role for me. Quite soon I began to take on responsibilities. That was a social life.

I had thought I would take up art in a big way, that this at last was my moment. In fact I didn't. I did do some – a whole series of drawings that were quite cathartic, on the theme of caring for my mother. I think at first I was just enjoying having some free time: going to visit friends and having a very sociable time.

I threw myself into frantic activity – making up for lost time.

Do you think potential employers see that time you spent
looking after your mother as time well spent?

Helen

I think they probably regard it the same as looking after children – as a
total waste of time. I don't think they see it as anything good. I think it
ought to be the equivalent of industrial experience. People who have
had industrial experience are looked on as people with an asset, but
people who have spent time looking after children or old people – it
doesn't count for anything . . . it seems a bit illogical.

Did you feel with the end of caring you had lost an important
role in life?

Helen

No, because I had a family and that was my chief concern. My children
were aged 22, 20, 17, 13 and 8 at the time. It had always been hard
weighing up everyone's needs. Looking after my mother was almost
something I did in my spare time! It was on top of everything else. I
had enough other interests – but the difficulty was it made me resent
the time I had to spend with her because there were so many other
things to be done.

So what are you doing now?

Helen

Since I didn't get a job I became a volunteer. I help other carers, which
helps me to feel that all those years weren't wasted. It's a way of
putting that experience to good use. For me it was eight years of my
life when I might have been doing more profitable things. I didn't want
to just see it disappear. Even so, I do feel that in many ways those
years were a waste and that maybe I was a fool to do it.

Do you feel you had choice?

Helen

No.

So how do you feel about it now, five years later?

Helen

I still feel a lot of anger and resentment and anger at myself to have
allowed that situation to have developed and not fought against it hard

enough. The feelings that you have while caring don't just go away when the person dies. In fact, they go on more freely than ever, because now that person isn't there to answer back and you can go on having those dialogues in your head. It never ends.

Helen's experience of caring left her physically injured and with feelings of regret that she had lost opportunities to lead her own life while caring for her mother.

Other carers feel good about their days of caring and are able to make the transition to a new life easily. There is no norm. But with so few supporting services in the community, many people have embarked on caring because they felt they had no choice.

As Helen points out, if she had been injured at work she would have received compensation for her injury. But because caring is unpaid and largely unrecognised as physically and emotionally demanding work, people who are carers have to pay the price with their own health. This lack of recognition by society at large can make it difficult to value the importance of the work you have done while caring. As one carer said, 'Because there is no recognition, carers don't know they are doing anything good – in fact they are constantly judging themselves as failures because they aren't doing all the things they feel they ought to be doing.'

People who are, or have been, carers are campaigning for better treatment through organisations like the Carers National Association. They want to see carers receive an income that reflects their caring responsibilities; flexible employment which allows time off to care at home and opportunities to return to work; back-up services and support in the community; and readily available respite and residential care which can respond to individual and cultural diversity. Carers also need to know that when they can no longer shoulder the responsibility, there are reliable and high quality alternatives to home care.

Much of the exhaustion suffered by carers is aggravated by the need to battle with a system which has been cumbersome and slow to respond to carers' needs. Recent changes in community care will go some way to redress these problems. In the meantime, carers still have to be assertive in asking for the help they need.

Choice is essential if people are to feel that caring is a positive experience. That means a choice about whether to take on the caring in the first place and choice about the kind of support you can expect to receive. It is important for the self-respect of the person being cared for as well as for the carer. Some choices can only be brought about by changes in government policy. But others are in your hands.

This book shows you how other people have coped with caring in very difficult circumstances. None of them want to be seen as saints – just ordinary people doing the best they can. Their stories were willingly contributed because many feel passionately that an understanding of the difficulties which they encountered will help other carers to cope with their own situation. Their message is a simple one: that while caring for others is something to take pride in, you also have a right to a full and happy life of your own.

Appendix 1 Who does what? A glossary of job titles

Job titles can be confusing. Some titles may vary according to where you live, but here is a selection of some you may come across both in the community and in hospital.

Anaesthetists. A physician specialising in anaesthetic drugs and the care of the unconscious patient. Because of their expertise in relieving the pain of surgery, they are often involved with patients in intensive care or patients who need control of intractable pain where all else has failed.

Auxiliary nurse, see also Nursing auxiliary. An unqualified assistant who will probably have had some training in a hospital and will be able to do most of the general caring tasks, but is unlikely to give injections, etc.

Befriender. A volunteer who will spend social time with a person who might otherwise be restricted in making social contact.

Buddy. A volunteer befriender, usually linking up with someone who has HIV/AIDS.

Care assistant. In some areas a care assistant combines the tasks of the home help and nursing auxiliary to provide personal assistance with bathing as well as with household activities.

Care attendant. A person who comes into the home to take over the care and give the carer a break, *see* Crossroads Care Attendant Schemes, page 53.

Care manager. A person appointed by the local authority who is responsible for identifying people in need of community care services, and for planning and securing the delivery of services.

Cardiologist. A hospital specialist in diseases of the heart.

Chiropodist. Someone who provides foot care. Foot care assistants offer a simpler range of services – toe nail cutting, etc. Most chiropodists are in private practice.

Citizen advocate. Someone, usually a volunteer, who helps another person (often someone with a learning difficulty) to defend or exercise their rights.

Community care aide, see Home help.

Community hospice nurse. (In some areas only) a person specially trained in treatment and care of people who are terminally ill – pain management, sleeplessness, etc.

Community physiotherapist. A person who provides treatment aimed at relieving pain and restoring mobility. Can teach the carer ways of lifting without causing strain. (Usually works from the hospital physiotherapy department.)

Community psychiatric nurse (CPN). A nurse with special training who can help support people with mental health problems in their home.

Continence adviser. A specialist nurse who offers advice about the management of incontinence and how to get hold of useful aids and provisions.

Counsellor. A professional listener who offers emotional support to enable people to talk about their emotional difficulties and help them to work out their own ways of dealing with problems.

Dermatologist. A specialist in diseases of the skin.

Doctor (or general practitioner (GP), as s/he is also called). Deals with the general day-to-day medical problems of the person you look after. S/he should also check that *you* are managing without strain. Your family doctor can refer the person you look after to a hospital consultant for specialist care. S/he can also arrange for you to receive community nursing services.

Domiciliary dentist. A dentist who gives treatment in the home.

Domiciliary optician. An optician who gives treatment in the home.

District nurse. A general nurse with extra training in nursing at home. Will advise on day-to-day care – mobility, lifting and turning, hygiene, mouth care, bladder and bowel function, minor medical disorders. Will perform practical nursing tasks – dressings, giving injections, enemas, etc. and can also advise on incontinence and getting other help.

ENT surgeon. A surgeon who deals with surgery to the ears, nose and throat.

Family aide, see Home help.

Gastroenterologist. A specialist in digestive disorders.
Geriatrician. A specialist in diseases among elderly people.

Haematologist. A specialist in diseases of the blood.
Health visitor. A nurse whose role is to advise on health aspects
   of caring at home with the aim of anticipating and preventing
   new health problems. Tends to work mainly with parents of
   small children. A few specialise in working with elderly
   people.
Home help/ Home care assistant. Used to help with general
   household tasks and shopping. Their role is now changing to
   more involvement in helping with personal care in the home.
   Sometimes called Community care aide/Family aide.

Macmillan Nurse. (In some areas only) a nurse specially trained
   in the treatment and care of cancer. Funded by the Cancer
   Relief Macmillan fund but working within the NHS.

Neurologist. A specialist in diseases of the brain and nervous
   system.
Night nurse. A nurse who will stay overnight usually only with
   people who are terminally ill (*very* thin on the ground).
Nursing auxiliary, see Auxiliary nurse. An assistant to the district
   nurse. Carries out basic nursing tasks such as bathing.

Occupational therapist. Someone who assesses the condition of
   the person you care for *and* your own ability to cope.
   Provides aids such as wheelchairs, commodes, bath aids, etc.
   Can advise about adaptations to the home and how to get a
   grant from the housing department. Some OTs take on other
   responsibilities, e.g. running a stroke club.
Orthopaedic surgeon. A surgeon who deals with injuries to bones,
   tendons, ligaments and joints.

Paediatrician. A specialist in diseases and disability among
   children.
Physiotherapist, see Community physiotherapist.
Psychiatrist. A specialist in mental disorders for all age groups.
Psychogeriatrician. A specialist in mental disorders of elderly people.
Practice nurse. A nurse attached to a doctor's practice who may
   be able to offer, at the surgery, some of the services which
   district nurses and health visitors offer in the community.
   Every practice is different and you should ask what other

services are available. Some offer access to counsellors, foot-care, dietary advice or run clinics for particular problems.

Radiotherapist (and oncologist). A specialist in the treatment of cancer.

Receptionist (doctor's surgery). A person who takes messages, makes appointments and runs the office at the surgery and can often provide a wealth of advice on the availability of services locally.

Rheumatologist. A specialist in diseases of joints and muscles.

Sitter. Someone who will come into the home to give the carer a break. Usually does not take on nursing tasks.

Social worker. A person who is trained to assess the social and family situation. S/he can arrange day care and residential care and should provide information about claiming DSS benefits and other help available from the local authority, the health services as well as private and voluntary organisations. S/he can refer you to other services, according to what is available in your area.

Speech therapist. A person trained to help with speech or language disorders – particularly with children but also, for instance, with patients suffering speech difficulties following strokes. Most are based at schools or health centres but they sometimes make home visits.

State registered nurse/registered general nurse (SRN/RGN). A fully qualified nurse who can look after very ill or disabled clients. Able to administer medication and carry out all nursing tasks as well as everyday caring tasks such as washing, dressing or eating. Some work privately.

State enrolled nurse (SEN). A nurse who has the same practical nursing training as above. The difference is that SRN/RHNs go on to supervision and management training.

Urologist. A surgeon who deals with surgery to the kidneys and bladder.

Appendix 2 Further reading

Information and advice

CLYNE. R. *Coping with Cancer*, Thorsons, 1986.

DARBY, C. *Keeping Fit while Caring*, Family Welfare Association, 1984. A fully illustrated guide to lifting and handling a disabled person.

DISABILITY ALLIANCE ERA *Disability Rights Handbook*, Disability Alliance Educational and Research Association, 1990. A comprehensive guide to legal and welfare rights.

JEE, M. *Taking a Break*, Kings Fund, 1987, available free to carers from Taking a Break, Newcastle-upon-Tyne X, NE85 2AQ. Gives advice about how to go about finding respite care; how to find information on all types of breaks, both at home and away from home; how to make the practical arrangements; and how to cope with mixed feelings.

KOHNER, N. *Caring at Home*, National Extension College, 3rd edition, 1989. A very thorough and practical handbook for carers.

MACDONALD, FIONA. *The Health Directory*, Bedford Square Press, 1990.

MACE, N.L., RABINS, P.V. *The 36-Hour Day: Caring at Home for Confused Elderly People*. Hodder and Stoughton, 1985. A guide to dealing with the daily problems of caring for someone with Alzheimer's disease.

NCVO. *The Voluntary Agencies Directory*, Bedford Square Press, 1990.

ORTON, C. *Care for the Carer*, Thorsons, 1989. For carers of elderly people, advice on how to improve your own life, as well as practical sections on dealing with disability.

RICHARDSON, D. *Women and the AIDS crisis*, Pandora, 1987. 2nd edition 1989. A clear, straightforward account of the risks for women. Particularly useful for women caring for a relative with AIDS.

SINCLAIR, L. *Proper Channels*, MIND, 1987. A practical guide to complaints about medical treatment.

TORREY, DR E.F. *Surviving Schiozophrenia – A Family Manual*, Harper & Row, 1988.

Carers' experiences

BRIGGS, A., OLIVER, J. (eds). *Caring: Experiences of Looking After Disabled Relatives*, Routledge & Kegan Paul, 1985. One of the first books to identify carers' shared difficulties through carers' own testimony.

HICKS, C. *Who Cares?*, Virago Press, 1988. Based on over 80 interviews, explores the difficulties carers have to confront and examines the current government's record on supporting carers.

PITKEATHLEY, J. *It's My Duty Isn't It?*, Souvenir Press, 1989. Written by the director of the Carers National Association, the book is written to help carers as well as to draw attention to the reality behind 'care in the community'.

UNGERSON, C. *Policy is Personal: Sex, Gender and Informal Care*, Tavistock Publications, 1987. Examines some of the issues about the private and public faces of care within a feminist framework.

Autobiographies

MURPHY, D. *Wheels within Wheels*, John Murray, 1979. The story of a childhood in Ireland and looking after an elderly parent before taking off to India on a bicycle.

SLACK, P., MULVILLE, F. *Sweet Adeline: A Journey through Care*, Macmillan Education, 1988. A positive and heartwarming account of how the authors overcame the practical and emotional challenges of caring for Adeline, Patricia Slack's mother. Full of useful tips.

For people working with carers

BELL, R., GIBBONS, S. *Working with Carers*, Health Education Authority, 1989. Includes information, training activities for people working with carers of elderly people.

RICHARDSON, A., UNELL, J., ASTON. B. *A New Deal for Carers*, King's Fund Centre, 1989. A framework for understanding carers' needs and practical ways of meeting them.

Setting up self-help groups

ERNST, S., GOODISON, L. *In Our Own Hands*, The Women's Press Ltd, 1981. A book of self-help therapy.

WILSON, J. *Caring Together*. National Extension College and King's Fund, 1988. Practical guidelines for carers' self-help and support groups covering how to get your own group together, how to attract members, how to organise publicity, etc.

Appendix 3 Useful addresses

National organisations

If you are not sure which organisation to go to, start by contacting the Carers National Association.

Action for the Victims of Medical Accidents (AVMA)
Bank Chambers
1 London Road
Forest Hill
London SE23 3TO
Tel. 081-291 2793

Age Concern England
Bernard Sunley House
60 Pitcairn Road
Mitcham
Surrey CR4 3LL
Tel. 081-640 5431

Alzheimer's Disease Society
158-160 Balham High Road
London SW12 9BN
Tel. 081-675 6557

Arthritis Care
6 Grosvenor Crescent
London SW1X 7ER
Tel. 071-235 0902

Association of Crossroads Care Attendant Schemes
10 Regent Place
Rugby
Warwickshire CV21 2PN
Tel. 0788-73653

Association for All Speech Impaired Children (AFASIC)
347 Central Markets
London EC1A 9NH
Tel. 071-236 3632

Association to Aid Sexual and Personal Relationships of People with a Disability (SPOD)
286 Camden Road
London N7 0BJ
Tel. 071-607 8851/2

British Association of Cancer United Patients (BACUP)
121–123 Charterhouse Street
London EC1M 6AA
Tel. 071-608 1661

British Association for Counselling
37a Sheep Street
Rugby
Warwickshire CV21 3BX
Tel. 0788-78328/9

British Association of Psychotherapists
121 Hendon Lane
London N3 3PR
Tel. 081-346 1747

British Limbless Ex-Servicemen's Association (BLESMA)
Frankland Moore House
185–7 High Road
Chadwell Heath
Essex RM6 6NA
Tel. 081-590 1124/5

British Red Cross Society
9 Grosvenor Crescent
London SW1X 7EJ
Tel. 071-235 5454

British Sports Association for the Disabled
Haward House
Barnard Crescent
Aylesbury
Bucks
HP21 9PP
Tel. 0296-27889

Brook Advisory Centres
33 Tottenham Court Road
London W1A 9AE
Tel. 071-580 2991

Cancerlink
17 Britannia Street
London WC1X 9JN
Tel. 071-833 2451

Carers National Association
29 Chilworth Mews
London W2 3RG
Tel. 071-724 7776

Chest Heart and Stroke Association
Tavistock House North
Tavistock Square
London WC1H 9JE
Tel. 071-387 3012

College of Health
18 Victoria Park Square
London E2 9PF
Tel. 081-980 6263

COMBAT (Association to Combat Huntingdon's Chorea)
34a Station Road
Hinckley
Leicestershire LE10 1AP
Tel. 0455-61558

Commission for Racial Equality
Elliot House
10–12 Allington Street
London SW1E 5EH
Tel. 071-828 7022

Compassionate Friends
6 Denmark Street
Bristol BS1 5DQ
Tel. 0272-292778

Contact a Family
16 Strutton Ground
London SW1P 2HP
Tel. 071-222 2695

Counsel and Care for the Elderly
Twyman House
16 Bonny Street
London NW1 9PG
Tel. 071-485 1566 (Casework Department)

Cystic Fibrosis Research Trust
Alexandra House
5 Blyth Road
Bromley
Kent BR1 3RS
Tel. 081-464 7211

Cruse – Bereavement Care
126 Sheen Road
Richmond
Surrey TW9 1UR
Tel. 081-940 4818

DIAL UK (Disablement Information and Advice Lines)
Victoria Buildings
117 High Street
Clay Cross
Chesterfield
Derbyshire S45 9DZ
Tel. 0246-250055

Disability Alliance Educational and Research Association
25 Denmark Street
London WC2H 8NJ
Tel. 071-240 0806

Disabled Living Foundation
380–384 Harrow Road
London W9 2HU
Tel. 071-289 6111

Downs' Syndrome Association
12–13 Clapham Common
South Side
London SW4 7AA
Tel. 071-720 0008

Forces Help Society
122 Brompton Road
London SW3 1JE
Tel. 071-589 3243

Headway (National Head Injuries Association Ltd)
200 Mansfield Road
Nottingham NG1 3HX
Tel. 0602-622382

Help the Aged
16–18 St James Walk
London EC1R 0BE
Tel. 071-253 0253

Invalid Children's Aid Nationwide (ICAN)
198 City Road
London EC1V 2PH
Tel. 071-608 2462

Marie Curie Memorial Foundation
28 Belgrave Square
London SW1X 8QG
Tel. 071-235 3325

MENCAP (Royal Society for Mentally Handicapped Children and Adults)
123 Golden Lane
London EC1Y 0RT
Tel. 071-253 9433

MIND (National Association for Mental Health)
22 Harley Street
London W1N 2ED
Tel. 071-737 0741

Motor Neurone Disease Association
61 Derngate
Northampton NN1 1UE
Tel. 0604-22269/250505

Multiple Sclerosis Society of Great Britain
Nattrass House
35 Macaulay Road
London SW4 0QP
Tel. 071-720 8055

National Aids Helpline
Tel. 0800-567 123
(24-hour service)

National Association of Funeral Directors
618 Warwick Road
Solihull
West Midlands B91 1AA
Tel. 021-711 1343

National Association of Young People's Counselling and Advisory Services
17–23 Albion Street
Leicester LE1 6GD
Tel. 0533 558763

National Citizen Advocacy
2 St Pauls Road
London N1 2QR
Tel. 071-359 8289

National Council for Voluntary Organisations
26 Bedford Square
London WC1B 3HU
Tel. 071-636 4066

National Portage Association
(National Secretary)
4 Clifton Road
Winchester
Hants
Tel. 0962-60148

National Schizophrenia Fellowship
78 Victoria Road
Surbiton
Surrey KT6 4NS
Tel. 081-390 3651

Parkinson's Disease Society
36 Portland Place
London W1N 3DG
Tel. 071-255 2432

Patients Association
18 Victoria Park Square
Bethnal Green
London E2 9PF
Tel. 081-981 5676/5695

Play Matters/National Toy Libraries Association
68 Churchway
London NW1 1LT
Tel. 071-387 9592

Relate – National Marriage Guidance
Herbert Gray College
Little Church Street
Rugby
Warwicks CV21 3AP
Tel. 0788-73241

Royal Association for Disability and Rehabilitation (RADAR)
25 Mortimer Street
London W1N 8AB
Tel. 071-637 5400

Royal National Institute for the Blind
224 Great Portland Street
London W1N 6AA
Tel. 071-388 1266

Royal National Institute for the Deaf
105 Gower Street
London WC1E 6AH
Tel. 071-387 8033

St Johns Ambulance
1 Grosvenor Crescent
London SW1X 7EF
Tel. 071-235 5231

SENSE (National Deaf-Blind and Rubella Association)
311 Gray's Inn Road
London WC1X 8PT
Tel. 071-278 1005

Soldiers, Sailors and Airmen Family Association (SSAFA)
16–18 Old Queen Street
London SW1H 9HP
Tel. 071-222 9221

Spastics Society
12 Park Crescent
London W1N 4EQ
Tel. 071-636 5020

Spinal Injuries Association
Newpoint
76 St James's Lane
London N10 3DF
Tel. 081-444 2121

Sue Ryder Foundation
Sue Ryder Homes
Cavendish
Sudbury
Suffolk CO10 8AY
Tel. 0787-280252

Terrence Higgins Trust
52–54 Gray's Inn Road
London WC1X 8LT
Tel. 071-831 0330

Voluntary Council for Handicapped Children
National Children's Bureau
8 Wakley Street
London EC1V 7QE
Tel. 071-278 9441

Women's Royal Voluntary Service
234–244 Stockwell lRoad
London SW9 9SP
Tel. 071-733 3388

Women's Therapy Centre
6 Manor Gardens
London N7 6LA
Tel. 071-263 6200

Organisations in Northern Ireland

Some of these agencies are regional offices, with the national headquarters in London. Others are unique to Northern Ireland. For help with finding the right organisation, contact the regional Carers National Association or the Northern Ireland Council on Disability.

Age Concern Northern Ireland
6 Lower Crescent
Belfast BT7 1NR
Tel. 0232-245729

Alzheimer's Disease Society
113 University Street
Belfast BT7 1HP
Tel. 0232-439192

Association of Crossroads Care Attendant Schemes Northern Ireland Branch Secretary
20 Belvedere Park
Stranmillis
Belfast BT9 5GS
Tel. 0232-668526

Carers National Association
113 University Street
Belfast
Tel. 0232-439843

Chest Heart and Stroke Association
21 Dublin Road
Belfast BT2 7HN
Tel. 0232-320184

Extra Care for the Elderly
11a Wellington Park
Belfast BT10 6DJ
Tel. 0232-683273

Help the Aged
Lesley House
Shaftesbury Square
Belfast BT2 7DL
Tel. 0232-644914

MENCAP
Segal House
4 Annadale Avenue
Belfast BT7 3JH
Tel. 0232-691351

Northern Ireland Association for Counselling
Buryson House
28 Bedford Street
Belfast BT2 7FE
Tel. 0232-325835

Northern Ireland Association for Mental Health
80 University Street
Belfast BT7 1HE
Tel. 0232-328474

Northern Ireland Council for Disability
2 Annadale Avenue
Belfast BT7 3JH
Tel. 0232-491011

Northern Ireland Council for Voluntary Action
127 Ormeau Road
Belfast BT7 1SH
Tel. 0232-321224

APPENDIX 3 – USEFUL ADDRESSES 135

Organisations in Scotland

Some of these agencies are regional offices, with the national headquarters in London. Others are unique to Scotland. For help with finding the right organisation, contact the Scottish Council for Voluntary Organisations (SVCO) or the regional branch of the Carers National Association.

Age Concern Scotland
54a Fountainbridge
Edinburgh EH3 9PT
Tel. 031-228 5656

Alzheimer's Disease Society Scotland
1st Floor
40 Shandwick Place
Edinburgh EH2 4RT
Tel. 031-225 1453

Arthritis Care
Balbeg
Straiton
Maybole
Ayrshire KA19 7NN
Tel. 0655-7644

Association of Continence Advisers
Frances Bayiat
Longmore Hospital
Salisbury Place
Edinburgh EH9 1SJ
Tel. 031-667 0251

Association of Crossroads Care Attendant Schemes
24 George Square
Glasgow G2 1EG
Tel. 041-226 3793

Association for Counselling (Scotland)
re-organising under the title of COSCA: address can be supplied through SVCO (see page 137)

British Red Cross Society
Alexandra House
204 Bath Street
Glasgow G23 4HL
Tel. 041-332 9591

Cancer Relief Macmillan Fund
BMA House
7 Drumsheugh Gardens
Edinburgh EH3 7QJ
Tel. 031-229 3276

Cancerlink
9 Castle Terrace
Edinburgh EH1 2DP
Tel. 031-228 5567

Carers National Association (Scotland)
6 London Road
Kilmarnock
Ayrshire KA3 7AD
Helpline Mon-Fri, 1.30pm–3.30pm
Tel. 0563-43882

Chest Heart and Stroke Association
65 North Castle Street
Edinburgh EH2 3LT
Tel. 031-225 6963

Compassionate Friends
c/o 7 North Gyle Avenue
Edinburgh EH12 8JS
Tel. 031-339 2981

Cruse – Bereavement Care
138 McDonald Road
Edinburgh EH7 4NL
Tel. 031-556 4489

Disabled Drivers' Association
51 Margaretvale Drive
Larkhall
Lanarkshire ML9 1QH
Tel. 0698-881201

**Epilepsy Association of
Scotland**
48 Govan Road
Glasgow G51 1JL
Tel. 041-427 4911

Frontliners
37–39 Montrose Terrace
Edinburgh EH7 5DJ
Tel. 031-652 0754

**Forces Help Society and Lord
Roberts Workshops**
New Haig House
Logie Green Road
Ediburgh EH7 4HQ
Tel. 031-5571045

Headway Head Injuries Trust
Social Work Department
Southern General Hospital
Govan Road
Glasgow G51 4TF
Tel. 041-445 2466 ext 4150

Help the Aged
53 Black Friar Street
Edinburgh EH1 1NB
Tel. 031-556 4666

**Marie Curie Memorial
Foundation**
21 Rutland Street
Edinburgh EH1 2AH
Tel. 031-229 8332

**Multiple Sclerosis Society in
Scotland**
27 Castle Street
Edinburgh EH2 3DN
Tel. 031-225 3600

**Muscular Dystrophy Group of
Great Britain and Northern
Ireland**
Room 262
11 Bothwell Street
Glasgow G2 6LY
Tel. 041-221 4411

**National Schizophrenia
Fellowship Scotland**
40 Shandwick Place
Edinburgh EH2 4RT
Tel. 031-226 2025

Nucleus
18 London Road
Edinburgh EH7 5AT
Tel. 031-652 0168

Parkinson's Disease Society
10 Dunsmuir Court
Edinburgh EH12 7TD
Tel. 031-334 5718

**Physically Handicapped and
Able-Bodied Scotland**
Princes House
5 Shandwick Place
Edinburgh EH2 4RG
Tel. 031-229 3559

Royal National Institute for the Blind (RNIB)
9 Viewfield Place
Stirling FK8 1NL
Tel. 0786-51752

Royal National Institute for the Deaf (RNID)
Scientific and Technical
Department
9 Clairmont Gardens
Glasgow G3 7LW
Tel. 041-332 0343

Scottish Aids Monitor
PO Box 48
Edinburgh EH1 3SA
Tel. 031-557 3885

Scottish Association for Mental Health
Atlantic House
38 Gardners Crescent
Edinburgh EH3 8DQ
Tel. 031-229 9687

Scottish Council for Voluntary Organisations (SVCO)
18–19 Claremont Crescent
Edinburgh EH7 4OD
Tel. 031-556 3882

Scottish Council on Disability
Princes House
5 Shandwick Place
Edinburgh EH2 4RG
Tel. 031-2298632

Scottish Downs Syndrome Association
54 Shandwick Place
Edinburgh EH2 4RT
Tel. 031-226 2420

Scottish Motor Neurone Disease Association
Suite 11
136 Ingram Street
Glasgow G1 1EG
Tel. 041-552 0507

Scottish Society for the Mentally Handicapped
13 Elmbank Street
Glasgow G2 4QA
Tel. 041-226 4541

Scottish Spina Bifida Association
190 Queensferry Road
Edinburgh EH4 2BW
Tel. 031-332 0743

Scottish Spinal Cord Injury Association
Unit 22
100 Elderpark Street
Glasgow G51 3TR
Tel. 041-440 0960

Scottish Sports Association for the Disabled
Fife Institute of Physical and
Recreational Education
Viewfield Road
Glenrothes
Fife KY6 2RA
Tel. 0592-771700

SENSE in Scotland
168 Dumbarton Road
Glasgow G11 6XE
Tel. 041-334 9666/9675

Soldiers Sailors and Airmen Family Association (SSAFA)
New Haig House
Logie Green
Edinburgh EH7 4HQ
Tel. 031-557 1697

**St Andrew's Ambulance
Association**
St Andrews House
Milton Street
Glasgow G4 0HR
Tel. 041-332 4031

**Volunteer Development
Scotland**
80 Murray Place
Stirling FK8 2BX
Tel. 0786-79593

**Women's Royal Voluntary
Service**
Scottish Headquarters
19 Grosvenor Crescent
Edinburgh EH12 5EL
Tel. 031-337 2261

Organisations in Wales

Some of these agencies are regional offices, with the national
headquarters in London. Others are unique to Wales. For help
with finding the right organisation, contact the Wales Council
for Voluntary Action (WCVA) or the regional contact for the
Carers National Association.

Age Concern Wales
4th Floor
1 Cathedral Road
Cardiff CF1 9SD
Tel. 0226-371821

Alzheimer's Disease Society
13 Richmond Street
Cardiff CF2 3AH
Tel. 0222-493710

Arthritis Care
233 Western Avenue
Sandfields
Port Talbot
West Glamorgan SA12 7NE
Tel. 0639-886249

**Association of Crossroads
Care Attendant Schemes**
Watton Chambers
The Watton
Brecon
Powys LD3 YES
Tel. 0874-3090

British Red Cross (Wales)
Parc Y Bryn
Broadlay
Ferryside
Dyfed SA17 5UB
Tel. 026785-532

Cancer Crisis Centre Wales
13 Hanover Street
Canton
Cardiff
South Glamorgan CF5 1LS
Tel. 0222-395572

Cancer Relief Macmillan Fund
Conifers
St Nicholas
South Glamorgan
Tel. 0446-760245

Cruse - Bereavement Care
Yew Tree Cottage
West End
Magor
Newport
Gwent NP6 3HT
Tel. 0633-881380

Epilepsy Wales
Glan Ely Hospital
Fairwater
Cardiff
South Glamorgan
Tel. 0222-560975

Help the Aged
298 Gladstone Road
Barry
South Glamorgan CF6 6NH
Tel. 0446-745049

MENCAP (Wales)
169 City Road
Cardiff
South Glamorgan CF2 3JB
Tel. 0223-494933

MIND (Wales)
23 St Mary Street
Cardiff
South Glamorgan CF1 2AA
Tel. 0222-395123

Parkinson's Disease Society
Ceffyl Gwyn
Rhossili
Gower
West Glamorgan
Tel. 0792-390562

Spastics Society
382–384 Newport Road
Cardiff
South Glamorgan CF3 7UA
Tel. 0222-463420

Wales Council for the Blind
Shand House
20 Newport Road
Cardiff CF2 1JB
Tel. 0222-473954

Wales Council for the Deaf
Maritime Offices
Woodland Terrace
Maesycoed
Pontypridd
Mid-Glamorgan CF37 1DZ
Tel. 0443-485687

Wales Council for Voluntary Action
Llys Ifor
Crescent Road
Caerfili
Mid-Glamorgan CF8 1XL
Tel. 0222-809224 (also address for Wales Carers Campaign)

Women's Royal Voluntary Service (Wales HQ)
20 Cathedral Road
Cardiff
South Glamorgan CF1 9JJ
Tel. 0222-228386

Organisations concerned with respite and residential care

Many of the voluntary organisations above can advise you on respite care, and the Association of Crossroads Care Attendant Schemes runs its own service. Here are some additional organisations you might find useful (NB some will charge a fee for their service):

Carematch
286 Camden Road
London N7 0BJ
Tel. 071-609 9966
   Has a database of information about residential care for physically disabled people.

Caresearch
Second Floor
Kew Bridge House
Kew Bridge Road
Brentford
Middlesex TW8 0ED
Tel. 081-847 3971
   Has a database of information about residential care for people with learning difficulties.

Elderly Accommodation Counsel Ltd
1 Durward House
31 Kensington Court
London W8 5BH
Tel. 081-995 8320
   Has a register based on a national database of all forms of private and voluntary accommodation for elderly people. It does not place people or recommend establishments but will give information on the area of choice and within the price range requested for a small charge.

John Groom's Association for the Disabled
10 Gloucester Drive
Finsbury Park
London N4 2LP
Tel. 081-802 7272
   Runs projects to help disabled people including residential and holiday accommodation.

Holiday Care Service
2 Old Bank Chambers
Station Road
Horley
Surrey RH6 9HW
Tel. 0293-774535
   Advice on holidays and travel arrangements with helpers.

Hospice Information Service
St Christophers Hospice
51–59 Lawrie Park Road
Sydenham
London SE26 6DZ
Tel. 081-778 9252
   Free advice about hospice care.

Jewish Welfare Board
221 Golders Green Road
London NW11 9DW
Tel. 081-458 3282
  Runs residential and
  nursing homes for Jewish
  people.

National Care Association
8 Southampton Place
London WC1A 2EF
Tel. 071-405 2277
  More than 70 member
  associations of proprietors
  of private homes will offer
  advice on any matters
  regarding private residential
  care.

**Registered Nursing Home
Association**
Calthorpe House
Hagley Road
Edgbaston
Birmingham B16 8QY
Tel. 021-454 2511

Provides information on
registered nursing homes in
the United Kingdom and
the Republic of Ireland
which conform to certain
standards and which have
been visited by the
association. Their reference
book of homes is available
free of charge.

**United Kingdom Home Care
Association (UKHCA)**
c/o Care Alternatives Limited
206 Worple Road
Wimbledon
London SW20 8PN
Tel. 081-946 8202
  An association of private
  home-care providers aiming
  to set codes and standards
  of practice.

Index

Other titles in the **Survival Handbooks** series:

Shirley Cooklin
From Arrest to Release: The Inside/Outside Survival Guide

Neil Davidson
Boys Will Be . . . Sex Education and Young Men

Sandra Horley
Love and Pain: A Survival Handbook for Women

Tony Lake and Fran Acheson
*Room to Listen, Room to Talk: A Beginner's Guide to Analysis,
Therapy and Counselling*

Jacquelynn Luben
Cot Deaths: Coping with Sudden Infant Death Syndrome

For further details, please write to the sales manager, Bedford
Square Press, London WC1B 3HU

The Voluntary Agencies Directory

The Social Activists' Bible

NCVO's directory of voluntary agencies is the standard reference work for anyone who cares about helping the community. It lists nearly 2,000 leading voluntary agencies, ranging from small, specialist self-help groups to long-established national charities. It gives concise, up-to-date descriptions of their aims and activities, with details of

charitable status	local branches
volunteer participation	membership
trading activities	staffing

A list of useful addresses includes professional and public advisory bodies concerned with voluntary action; a classified index and quick reference list of acronyms and abbreviations give easy access to entries.

There is extensive coverage of new groups concerned with women's issues, minority rights, self-help, community development and leisure activities, environment and conservation, campaigning and consumer affairs.

Voluntary agencies play an important part in making the world a better place to live in. This NCVO directory is the essential guide to their work.

'If you buy only one directory of voluntary agencies, buy this one and buy it every year.' *Health Libraries Review*

'an essential working tool' *Environment Now*

The Health Directory
Compiled for the 'Thames Help' programme by
Fiona Macdonald

In association with the College of Health and the Patients Association

A new edition of the former *Health Help* volume, first published
by Bedford Square Press in 1987, the 1990/91 edition lists
around 1,000 organisations set up to help patients and their
families with many common (and not so common) health problems. They range from established national bodies such as the
Red Cross and the NSPCC, to self-help groups dealing with a
particular disorder.

Symbols are used to indicate when an organisation is a
registered charity, has branches or local groups, welcomes
volunteers or produces publications. The directory also includes
organisations dealing with complementary medicine, ethnic
minorities and general sources of help. The entries are listed
alphabetically and in a comprehensive index by subject area.

The Parents' Directory
Compiled by Fiona Macdonald
Foreword by Esther Rantzen

'Whatever the problem . . . you only need spend a few minutes glancing through the pages of *The Parents' Directory* to see what an astonishing variety of voluntary bodies there are for parents to turn to . . . an excellent and comprehensive map.'
Esther Rantzen

The Parents' Directory lists around 800 voluntary organisations which are able to give help, advice and information to parents on a wide range of topics. The information is presented in easily accessible form under the headings Education, Family Welfare, Handicap, Health and Leisure, with each entry giving details of aims and objects, contact names and telephone. Symbols are used to give additional information in the same manner as that outlined for the *Health Directory*.

Forthcoming

The Women's Directory
Compiled by Fiona Macdonald

The Women's Directory will enable women who wish to make contact with others – whether for social, cultural, sporting, charitable, self-help or political purposes – to locate and identify suitable groups and organisations. It refers women to appropriate 'umbrella' bodies, whether voluntary, local-government-based or state funded, and gives other sources of information about women's activities, including relevant magazines and journals, publishers and bookshops. Presented in an accessible, simple-to-follow format, with symbols used to give additional information in the same manner as that outlined for *The Health Directory*.